Guided Math Lessons in Kindergarten

Guided Math Lessons in Kindergarten provides detailed lessons to help you bring guided math groups to life. Based on the bestselling *Guided Math in Action*, this practical book offers 16 lessons, taught in a round of three—concrete, pictorial and abstract. The lessons are based on the priority standards and cover fluency, word problems, counting and cardinality, and place value. Author Dr. Nicki Newton shows you the content as well as the practices and processes that should be worked on in the lessons, so that students not only learn the content but also how to solve problems, reason, communicate their thinking, model, use tools, use precise language, and see structure and patterns.

Throughout the book, you'll find tools, templates and blackline masters so that you can instantly adapt the lesson to your specific needs and use it right away. With the easy-to-follow plans in this book, students can more work more effectively in small guided math groups—and have loads of fun along the way! Remember that guided math groups are about doing the math. So throughout these lessons you will see students working with manipulatives to make meaning, doing mathematical sketches to show what they understand and can make sense of the abstract numbers. When students are given the opportunities to make sense of the math in hands-on and visual ways, then the math begins to make sense to them!

Dr. Nicki Newton has been an educator for 30 years, working both nationally and internationally with students of all ages. She has worked on developing Math Workshop and Guided Math Institutes around the country; visit her website at www.drnickinewton.com. She is also an avid blogger (www.guidedmath.wordpress.com), tweeter (@drnickimath) and Pinterest pinner (www.pinterest.com/drnicki7).

Also Available from Dr. Nicki Newton
(www.routledge.com/eyeoneducation)

Guided Math Lessons in Kindergarten:
Getting Started

Day-by-Day Math Thinking Routines in Kindergarten:
40 Weeks of Quick Prompts and Activities

Day-by-Day Math Thinking Routines in First Grade:
40 Weeks of Quick Prompts and Activities

Day-by-Day Math Thinking Routines in Second Grade:
40 Weeks of Quick Prompts and Activities

Day-by-Day Math Thinking Routines in Third Grade:
40 Weeks of Quick Prompts and Activities

Day-by-Day Math Thinking Routines in Fourth Grade:
40 Weeks of Quick Prompts and Activities

Day-by-Day Math Thinking Routines in Fifth Grade:
40 Weeks of Quick Prompts and Activities

Leveling Math Workstations in Grades K–2:
Strategies for Differentiated Practice

Daily Math Thinking Routines in Action:
Distributed Practices Across the Year

Mathematizing Your School:
Creating a Culture for Math Success
Co-authored by Janet Nuzzie

Math Problem Solving in Action:
Getting Students to Love Word Problems, Grades K–2

Math Problem Solving in Action:
Getting Students to Love Word Problems, Grades 3–5

Guided Math in Action, Second Edition
Building Each Student's Mathematical Proficiency with Small-Group Instruction

Math Workshop in Action:
Strategies for Grades K–5

Math Running Records in Action:
A Framework for Assessing Basic Fact Fluency in Grades K–5

Math Workstations in Action:
Powerful Possibilities for Engaged Learning in Grades 3–5

Guided Math Lessons in Kindergarten

Getting Started

Dr. Nicki Newton

Routledge
Taylor & Francis Group

NEW YORK AND LONDON

First published 2022
by Routledge
605 Third Avenue, New York, NY 10158

and by Routledge
2 Park Square, Milton Park, Abingdon, Oxon, OX14 4RN

Routledge is an imprint of the Taylor & Francis Group, an informa business

© 2022 Nicki Newton

Library of Congress Cataloging-in-Publication Data
A catalog record for this book has been requested

ISBN: 978-0-367-77045-7 (hbk)
ISBN: 978-0-367-76004-5 (pbk)
ISBN: 978-1-003-16952-9 (ebk)

DOI: 10.4324/9781003169529

Typeset in Palatino
by Apex CoVantage, LLC

Contents

Meet the Author

Dr. Nicki Newton has been an educator for over 30 years, working both nationally and internationally, with students of all ages. Having spent the first part of her career as a literacy and social studies specialist, she built on those frameworks to inform her math work. She believes that math is intricately intertwined with reading, writing, listening and speaking. She has worked on developing Math Workshop and Guided Math Institutes around the country. Most recently, she has been helping districts and schools nationwide to integrate their State Standards for Mathematics and think deeply about how to teach these within a math workshop model. Dr. Nicki works with teachers, coaches and administrators to make math come alive by considering the powerful impact of building a community of mathematicians who make meaning of real math together. When students do real math, they learn it. They own it, they understand it, and they can do it. Every one of them. Dr. Nicki is also an avid blogger (www.guidedmath.wordpress.com), tweeter (@drnickimath) and Pinterest pinner (www.pinterest.com/drnicki7/). She speaks around the country and will virtually pop into any bookstudy if requested!

Contact her at:
Dr. Nicki Newton, Educational Consultant
Phone: 347–688–4927
Email: drnicki7@gmail.com

Find More Online!

Resources, videos, and conversations with Dr. Nicki can be found in the Guided Math Dropbox Resources: https://bit.ly/2Ja4sMY

Acknowledgments

I thank God for life and happiness. I thank my family and friends for all their support. I thank my editor Lauren who is the best in the world! I thank all the reviewers who gave feedback that helped make the series what it is! I thank the copyediting and production team for all their hard work.

I would also like to thank Math Learning Center (www.mathlearningcenter.org/apps), Braining Camp (www.brainingcamp.com/) and Didax (www.didax.com/math/virtual-manipulatives. html) for the use of screenshots of their fabulous virtual manipulatives.

www.brainingcamp.com/
www.mathlearningcenter.org/apps

1
Introduction

Figure 1.1 Guided Math Example

I pull a group of kindergartens who are working on their make ten facts. This particular group of students is still really shaky on making ten, so we are using the ten frame and playing a game where they have to build the number and then say how many more to 10. It provides them with a scaffold (which will eventually be phased out). They giggle with a sense of confidence as they build the fact and explain their thinking. When we are done, we talk about what we did and students give examples. They also talk about who thinks this is easy and who thinks it is tricky.

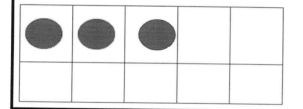

Figure 1.2 Guided Math Example 2

I pull a different group of kindergartners. We are working on a way to name numbers through 7. The students are picking dominos that show ways to make 7. They have to name the equation, for example: I pulled 3 and 4 and that makes 7.

Guided math is a small group instructional strategy that teaches students in their zone of proximal development around the priority standards. There are so many standards, but every state has priority focus standards. Those are the standards that you teach in a small guided math group. It is a time for hands-on, minds-on learning based on the standards. It is a time for discussing ideas, listening to the thinking of others, reasoning out loud and becoming a confident, competent mathematician.

Guided math groups are for everyone! Too often, students are rushed through big ideas, understandings and skills. They are left with ever widening gaps. Guided math groups give teachers the time needed to work with students in a way that they can all learn (see Figures 1.1 and 1.2). Guided math groups can be used to remediate, to teach on grade level concepts, and to address the needs of students who are working beyond grade level.

There are different ways that students can be grouped. Sometimes there are heterogeneous groups, and other times they are homogenous groups. Sometimes students are grouped by readiness. Other times students are grouped by interest or choice. So, for example, say you are working on object counting to 10, and half the class gets it and the other half is still struggling.

DOI: 10.4324/9781003169529-1

Figure 1.3 Visually Scaffolded Flashcards   **Figure 1.4** Unscaffolded Flashcards

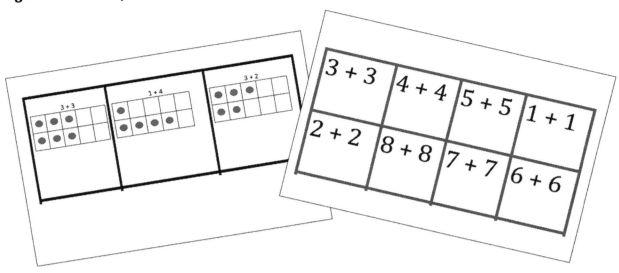

You might pull some temporary small groups and practice some hands-on lessons with counters for the students who are struggling, but that doesn't mean you will forget about the other kids. You could also pull another group of kids and play a counting card game (they are past needing the concrete scaffolds). You could have days where you pull a heterogeneous group and allow the kids who need the scaffolds to use them during the game. You could also have students work with different cards in a group (see Figures 1.3 and 1.4). One group might work with visually scaffolded cards and the other group with unscaffolded cards.

You could also ask students what they are interested in working on in small groups. You all would have a whole class discussion and generate a list of topics and then students would sign up for group sessions that they are interested in attending. The focus here is that the students generate the topics and then sign up for them. Another way to do this is to have the teacher think about different topics that the students need to work on, based on the data and then offer those topics to the students and they can sign up for which sessions that they want to attend.

Guided math groups can occur in all types of classrooms. Typically, they are part of a math workshop. In a math workshop (see Figure 1.5) there are three parts.

Opening:
♦ Energizers and routines
♦ Problem solving
♦ Mini-lesson

Student Activity
♦ Math workstations
♦ Guided math groups

Debrief
♦ Discussion
♦ Exit slip/exit ticket
♦ Mathematician's chair share

What Are the Other Kids Doing?

The other students should be engaged in some type of independent practice. They can be working alone, with partners or in small groups (see Figures 1.6 and 1.7). They could be rotating through stations based on a designated schedule or they could be working from a menu of must do's and can do's. The point is that students should be practicing counting, numbers, fluency, word problems and later in the year, place value. There should also be workstations focusing on the current unit of study. This work should be organized in a way that students are working

Figure 1.5 Math Workshop

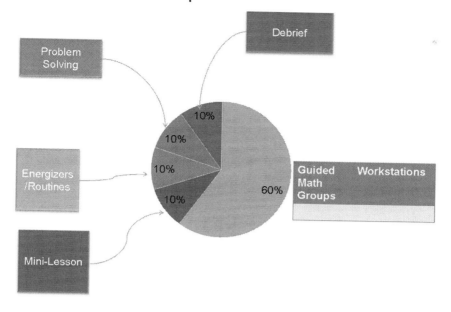

on in their zone of proximal development (Vygotsky, 1978). It is important spending time at the beginning of the year helping students to work in workstations independently (Figure 1.8).

Differentiating workstations helps to purposefully plan for the learning of all students. For example, the fluency workstation games should be divided by strategy; students can be working on either plus 1 facts, make 5 facts or make 10 facts (Baroody, 2006; Van de Walle, 2006; Henry & Brown, 2008). Another example is word problems. In most states, there are four single step problems that kindergarteners are exposed to. Knowing the learning trajectory and understanding the structures that go from simple to complex can help organize the teaching and learning of word problems (Carpenter, Fennema, Franke, Levi, & Empson, 1999/2015; Fuchs et al., 2010); Jitendra, Hoff, and Beck (1999).

Figures 1.6 and 1.7 Workstation Games

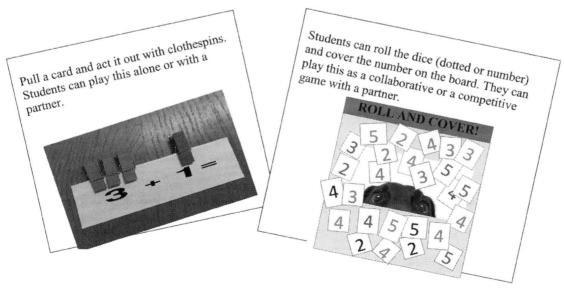

Figure 1.8 Workstation Contract

Workstation Contract

I have the privilege of learning with the Math Workstations.

I will play fair.

I will be a good sport. If I win, I will celebrate appropriately. If I lose, I'll be a good sport.

I will use the math manipulatives the way they are supposed to be used.

I will use the digital resources the way they are supposed to be used.

I will put everything back neatly.

I will work hard every day.

I will keep trying when the going gets tough!

My Signature:_____

Date: _____

Benefits of Guided Math Groups

- See student knowledge in action
- Monitor the concepts and skills that are understood
- Catch and address the misunderstandings
- Ask questions that highlight thinking
- Analyze thinking
- Listen to conversations
- Assess in the moment
- Redirect in the moment
- Differentiate as needed

Key Ideas

- Different reasons: relearn, focus on grade level topics or working beyond grade level
- Cycle of engagement: concrete, pictorial, abstract
- Heterogeneous and homogeneous grouping
- Math workshop
- Math workstations
- Benefits of guided math

Chapter Summary

Guided math is a great way to differentiate learning for all your students. Focus on the priority standards. Students approach these standards through a concrete, pictorial and abstract cycle of engagement. Sometimes, the groups are homogeneous groups and other times the groups are heterogeneous. Guided math groups can be done in a variety of ways, either traditional set-ups or a math workshop model. The other students should always be doing work that they are familiar with and are practicing in the math workstation. Many times, the work that students are working on in the guided math group is carried over into the math workstation. When the students are in guided math groups, the other students should be meaningfully engaged in math workstations or in some classrooms doing seatwork. All of this works together to give all students a chance to learn.

Reflection Questions

1. How are you differentiating instruction around the priority standards right now?
2. Currently, how do you group students? What informs your grouping?
3. Do you have a plan to make sure that everybody fully understands the priority standards?

References

Baroody, A. J. (2006). Why Children Have Difficulties Mastering the Basic Number Combinations and How to Help Them. *Teaching Children Mathematics*, 13, 22–32.

Carpenter, T. P., Fennema, E., Franke, M. L., Levi, L., & Empson, S. B. (1999/2015). *Children's Mathematics: Cognitively Guided Instruction*. Portsmouth, NH: Heinemann.

Fuchs, L., Zumeta, R., Schumacher, R., Powell, S., Seethaler, P., Hamlett, C., & Fuchs, D. (2010). The Effects of Schema-Broadening Instruction on Second Graders' Word-Problem Performance and Their Ability to Represent Word Problems with Algebraic Equations: A

Randomized Control Study. *Elementary School Journal*, 110(4), 446–463. Retrieved January 4, 2020 from https://www.ncbi.nlm.nih.gov/pubmed/20539822

Henry, V., & Brown, R. (2008, March). First-Grade Basics: An Investigation into Teaching and Learning of an Accelerated, High-Demand Memorization Standard. *Journal for Research in Mathematics Education*, 39(2), 153–183.

Jitendra, A. K., Hoff, K., & Beck, M. M. (1999). Teaching Middle School Students with Learning Disabilities to Solve Word Problems Using a Schema-Based Approach. *Remedial and Special Education*, 20(1), 50–64. https://doi.org/10.1177/074193259902000108

Van de Walle, J. A., & Lovin, L. A. H. (2006). *Teaching Student-Centered Mathematics: Grades 3–5*. Boston: Pearson.

Vygotsky, L. S. (1978). *Mind in Society: The Development of Higher Psychological Processes*. London: Harvard University Press.

2

Behind the Scenes

Assessment

Assessment is a crucial element in designing a guided math lesson. Teachers have to know where their students are along the trajectory of learning so that they can plan to teach them purposefully. Teachers need actionable data. Actionable data is data that can be used immediately to develop meaningful lessons. At the beginning of the year, teachers need to get data about the priority standards/major cluster standards from the year before so they can figure out if there are any gaps and make a plan to close them. Richardson notes, "The information gathered from the assessments helps teachers pinpoint what each child knows and still needs to learn. They are not about 'helping children be right,' but about uncovering their instructional needs" (n.d.). In the beginning of the year, we need to assess kindergarteners' sense of numbers and counting. Here is an example (see Figure 2.1).

Math Running Records is a great way to check fluency! These are done at the end of kindergarten. It's the GPS of fact fluency (see Figure 2.2). Remember, every summer, students lose at least 2.6 months of math (Shafer, 2016). Teachers should assess fluency, word problems, operations and algebraic thinking, and place value in the beginning of the year. At the middle of the year, teachers should assess all the grade level work done in these areas during the first part of the year. At the end of the year, teachers should assess all the priority standards for the grade. Throughout the year, teachers should rely on entrance and exit slips, quizzes, anecdotal notes, unit assessments and conferring to get information about students (see Figure 2.3).

Grouping

Guided math groups should have three to five students. I would like to reiterate again that sometimes they are heterogeneous groups and sometimes they are homogeneous groups. It depends on what you are trying to do. When we are thinking about grouping, it is about meeting the needs of the students where they are and taking them to what they need to learn at that grade level, so students are emerging in their learning along the continuum. It is about creating flexible groups that students can move through as they work on different concepts (see Figure 2.4). These groups should never be "fixed" and track students throughout the year. They are temporary, flexible, focused groups that teach students what they need, when they need it and then students move on to different work. Groups should last between 10 and 15 minutes. Remember the attention span rule: Age plus a few minutes.

DOI: 10.4324/9781003169529-2

Figure 2.1 Assessment Example

Assessment

Verbal Counting; Cardinality within 5

Question 1: Teacher: Can you count to 5?	Question 2: Teacher: Can you count to 10?
Circle the number the student can count to:	Circle the number the student can count to:

1	2	3	4	5

1	2	3	4	5	6	7	8	9	10

Question 3: Teachers sets out 3 counters on the table.
Teacher: Will you tell me how many counters there are?
When child finishes counting, ask "How many counters are there?"
Student Response:
Notice what the child does. Do they have to count again or do they know that the last number is the amount of the group?

Question 4: Teachers sets out 5 counters on the table.
Teacher: Will you tell me how many counters there are?
When child finishes counting, ask "How many counters are there?"
Student Response:
Notice what the child does. Do they have to count again or do they know that the last number is the amount of the group?

Question 5: Teachers shows the cards below (one at a time).
Teacher: Will you tell me how many counters there are on the card?
When child finishes counting, ask "How many counters are there?"
Student Response:
Notice what the child does. Do they have to count again or do they know that the last number is the amount of the group?

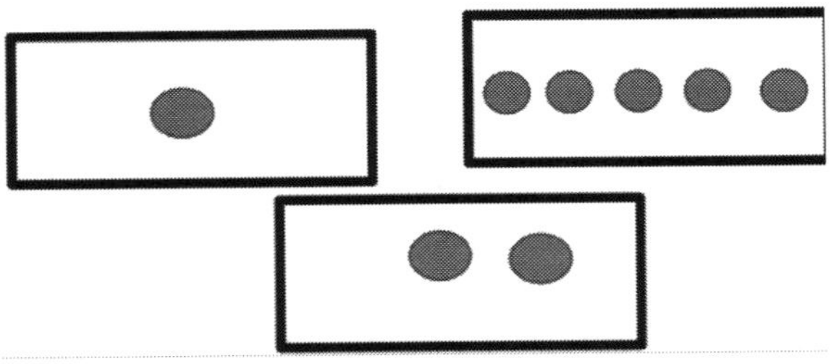

Question 6: Teachers shows the cards below (one at a time).
Teacher: Will you tell me how many counters there are on the card?
When child finishes counting, ask "How many counters are there?"
Student Response:
Notice what the child does. Do they have to count again or do they know that the last number is the amount of the group?

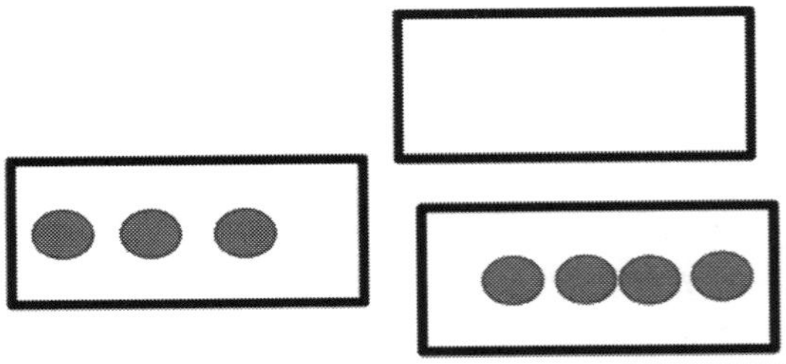

Figure 2.2 Addition Running Record Recording Sheet

Addition Running Record Recording Sheet

Student: _____ Teacher: _____ Date: _____

Part 1: Initial Observations
Teacher: We are now going to administer Part 1 of the Running Record. I am going to give you a sheet of paper with some problems. I want you to go from the top to the bottom and tell me just the answer. If you get stuck, you can stop and ask for what you need to help you. If you want to pass, you can. We might not do all of the problems. I am going to take notes so I remember what happened. Let's start.

Part 1	Codes: What do you notice?	Initial Observations of Strategies	Data Code Names
0 + 1 a 5s pth	ca fco cah coh wo sc asc dk	0 1 2 3 4M 4	A0----- add 0
2 + 1 a 5s pth	ca fco cah coh wo sc asc dk	0 1 2 3 4M 4	A1----- add 1
3 + 2 a 5s pth	ca fco cah coh wo sc asc dk	0 1 2 3 4M 4	Aw5--- add w/in 5
2 + 6 a 5s pth	ca fco cah coh wo sc asc dk	0 1 2 3 4M 4	Aw10—add w/in 10
4 + 6 a 5s pth	ca fco cah coh wo sc asc dk	0 1 2 3 4M 4	AM10---add making 10
10 + 4 a 5s pth	ca fco cah coh wo sc asc dk	0 1 2 3 4M 4	A10-----add 10 to a #
7 + 7 a 5s pth	ca fco cah coh wo sc asc dk	0 1 2 3 4M 4	AD------add doubles
5 + 6 a 5s pth	ca fco cah coh wo sc asc dk	0 1 2 3 4M 4	AD1-----add dbls +/-1
7 + 5 a 5s pth	ca fco cah coh wo sc asc dk	0 1 2 3 4M 4	AD2----add dbls +/-2
9 + 6 a 5s pth	ca fco cah coh wo sc asc dk	0 1 2 3 4M 4	AHF/C9-add higher facts use compensation w/9
8 + 4 a 5s pth	ca fco cah coh wo sc asc dk	0 1 2 3 4M 4	AHF/C7/8—add higher facts/use compensation with 7/8
7 + 8 a 5s pth	ca fco cah coh wo sc asc dk	0 1 2 3 4M 4	AHF/C7/8—add higher facts/use compensation with 7/8

Codes	Types of Strategies	Strategy Levels
a - automatic 5s - 5 seconds pth - prolonged thinking time	ca - counted all fco – finger counted on cah – counted all in head coh – counted on in head wo - wrong operation sc - self corrected asc - attempted to self-correct dk - didn't know	0 – doesn't know 1 – counting strategies by ones or skip counting using fingers, drawings or manipulatives 2 - mental math/solving in head 3 - using known facts and strategies 4M - automatic recall from memory 4 – automatic recall and students have number sense

(Continued)

Figure 2.2 (Continued)

Part 2: Flexibility/Efficiency
Teacher: We are now going to administer Part 2 of the Running Record. In this part of the Running Record we are going to talk about what strategies you use when you are solving basic addition facts. I am going to tell you a problem and then ask you to tell me how you think about it. I am also going to ask you about some different types of facts. Take your time as you answer and tell me what you are thinking as you see and do the math. I am going to take notes so I can remember everything that happened during this Running Record.

Add 0 0 + 1	Add 1 2 + 1	Add w/in 5 or 10 3 + 2 2 + 6	Add to Make 10 4 + 6
What happens when you add zero to a number? ___ same # ___other ___can't articulate What would be the answer to... 3 + 0 0 + 5 8 + 0	What strategy do you use when you add 1 to a number? ___ next counting # ___other ___can't articulate What would be the answer to.... 4 + 1 1 + 7 10 + 1	How do you solve 4 + 0? And 6 + 3? ___ count on from big # ___ other ___can't articulate w/in 5 _____ w/in 10 1 + 3 5 + 4 2 + 2 2 + 7	How do you solve 5 + 5? ___ count on from big # ___ other ___can't articulate **I'm going to give you a number and I want you to give me the number that makes 10 with it.** If I give you 7, how many more to make 10? If I give you ____ how many more to 10? 9? 2? 6? 3?
Do they know this strategy? No/Emerging/Yes A0 Level 0 1 2 3 4M 4	Do they know this strategy? No/Emerging/Yes A1 Level 0 1 2 3 4M 4	Do they know this strategy? No/Emerging/Yes A10 Level 0 1 2 3 4M 4	Do they know this strategy? No/Emerging/Yes AM10 Level 0 1 2 3 4M 4
Add 10 10 + 4	**Doubles 7 + 7**	**Doubles +/- 1 5 + 6**	**Doubles +/- 2 7 + 5**
What strategy do you use when you add 10 to a number? ___ teen #s decompose to 10 and 1's ___other ___can't articulate How would you solve ____? 10 + 2 10 + 6 10 + 8 Do they know this strategy?	How would you solve 6 + 6? ___ doubles ___ other ___can't articulate How would you solve _____? 4 + 4 8 + 8 9 + 9 What kind of facts are these? _____ Do they know this strategy?	How would you solve 6 + 7? ___ doubles +/-1 ___ other ___can't articulate How would you solve ____? 2 + 3 3 + 4 8 + 9 Do they know this strategy?	If a friend did not know how to solve 7 + 9, what would you tell her to do? ___ doubles +/-2 ___other ___can't articulate How would **you solve**....? 2 + 4 8 + 6 9 + 11 Do they know this strategy?
No/Emerging/Yes A10 Level 0 1 2 3 4M 4	No/Emerging/Yes AD Level 0 1 2 3 4M 4	No/Emerging/Yes AD1 Level 0 1 2 3 4M 4	No/Emerging/Yes AD2 Level 0 1 2 3 4M 4

Bridge through 10 (9) 9 + 6	Bridge through 10 (7/8) 8 + 4	Part 3: Mathematical Disposition
If your friend was stuck solving 9 + 5, what would you tell him to do? ___ bridge 10 ___other ___can't articulate How do you solve _____? 9 + 3 9 + 6	What strategy would you use to solve 8 + 3? ___ bridge 10 ___other ___can't articulate How would you solve ____? 4 + 7? 8 + 5?	Do you like math? What do you find easy? What do you find tricky? What do you do when you get stuck?
Do they know this strategy? No/Emerging/Yes AHF/C9 Level 0 1 2 3 4M 4	Do they know this strategy? No/Emerging/Yes AHF/C 7/8 Level 0 1 2 3 4M 4	Question Prompts: That's interesting/fascinating: tell me what you did. That's interesting/fascinating: tell me how you solved it. That's interesting/fascinating: tell me what you were thinking. How did you solve this problem? Can you tell me more about how you solve these types of problems? What do you mean when you say _____? (i.e. ten friends/neighbor numbers etc.)

General Observations (to be filled out after the interview)

Instructional Response:
Fluency Focus areas (circle all that apply): flexibility   efficiency   accuracy   automaticity

What addition strategy should the instruction focus on?

A0 A1 Aw5 Aw10 AM10 A10 AD AD1 AD2 AHF/C9 AHF/C 7/8

For his/her current instructional level, what is the predominant way in which the student is arriving at the answers? 0 1 2 3 4M 4 _____

Overall, what is the way in which the students calculated the answers?: 0 1 2 3 4M 4

Comments/Notes about gestures, behaviors, remarks:

*In most states k fluency is within 5 and 1st grade fluency is within 10 and 2nd grade within 20. However, some states k is within 10 and 1st and 2nd is within 20.

Figure 2.3 Exit Slip Example

1 + 2	0 + 5
3 + 2	4 + 1

Circle the easy problems. Underline the tricky ones.
How do you feel about addition?

Great	Good	Ok
☺	☺	☺

Figure 2.4 Types of Groups

Group 1: Emergent	Group 2: Early Fluent	Group 3: Fluent	Group 4: Advanced Fluent
These are the students who are working below grade level in some areas. They also have many strengths. We need to find their strengths and use them to help close gaps and misunderstandings. It is important to work on closing gaps as well as highly scaffolding (but not over scaffolding) current grade level material.	These students are approaching grade level. They have partial understanding of a concept or skill. So we must build on that understanding to close any gaps and address misunderstandings and misconceptions.	These students are right at grade level. Sometimes, these students have yet to have a deep understanding of the math. Sometimes, they can get the answer but they have trouble explaining what they did and why they did it.	These students are working above grade level. This doesn't mean that the work should be done from the next grade level though, as Kathy Richardson notes it is important to go deeper with concepts rather than to jump to the next ones.

Students can be emergent learners in one area and advanced fluent learners in another. These are not meant to be labels that stick with students all year. As Dr. Kim Reid always said, "Labels are for boxes." Although we need a way to describe how students are doing in particular areas, we must never categorize them with fixed labels.

"Rather than viewing some children as 'low' or 'behind' or 'lacking in skills,' kidwatching teachers view all children as creative, capable learners – on their way to 'achieving control over the conventions of [math]—always "in process" always moving forward . . . ' (Flukey, 1997, p. 219 cited in Owocki & Goodman, 2002)." Students move and develop along their own trajectory. With the appropriate scaffolding we can teach everybody and move them to achieving grade level standards and beyond.

Differentiation

After teachers get the data, they need to use it to differentiate (see Figure 2.5). Some of the work is to close the gaps. Some of the work is to accelerate the learning of the advanced students. Some of the work is to teach in the grade level zone. A big part of the differentiation aspect of guided math lessons is the concrete, pictorial and abstract cycle. Sometimes, students know the answer but do not necessarily understand the math. It is crucial to do quick assessments with students to make sure that they understand the math. For example, a student might know that $6 + 4$ is 10 by counting up. So, they can get an answer, but they don't have strategic competence. We want them to have flexibility with numbers and know that this is a *make 10 fact*. We would practice it in a variety of ways with manipulatives, with sketches and with the numbers. We would also have the students verbalize what they are doing and contextualize it by telling stories (NCTM, 2014).

Figure 2.5 Differentiation

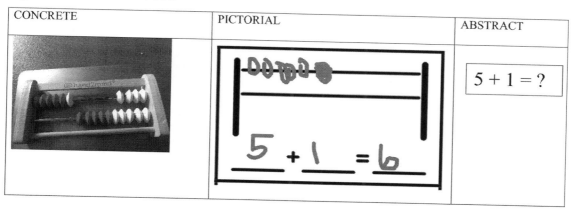

CONCRETE	PICTORIAL	ABSTRACT

Rotations

Teachers can assign students where they are going to go, visiting different stations every day. Another way to do it is to give the student a menu for the week with can do's and must do's. Either way, in kindergarten students should work on numbers, counting, geometry, eventually adding and subtracting within 5 (and later 10), word problems, place value (later in the year) and work from the current unit of study.

Standards-Based

Every guided math lesson should be centered around priority/readiness/power standards. There are so many standards to teach, so we have to focus. We have to get in there, dig deep and discuss ideas so that students can learn them. When students sit down in the group, the first thing the teacher should talk about is the work they are going to be doing for the day. The *I can* or *I am* learning to statement should be up and the students should discuss what they are going to be learning and what the criteria of success for that learning will look like. There is an ongoing discussion about whether to say *I can* or *I am* learning to. *I can* is more of a statement about what students will be able to do in the future. *I am learning to* speaks more to the continuum of learning and allows for students to be at different places along that continuum.

Dixon points out that sometimes, we shouldn't tell the students the *I can* statement at the beginning all of the time because then you in essence tell the ending of the story before it begins (2018a). This is an excellent point; it depends on where you are at in the concept and skill cycle and what the lesson of the day is. If you are trying to get students to explore and wonder about something, then don't upfront it, but discuss it at the end after they have explored the topic. However, if you are working on something that you have been doing for a while, you can say, "Today we are going to continue looking at . . . "

Depth of Knowledge

Guided math lessons are about building Depth of Knowledge with students. They should have questions from different levels, not just level one activities. For example, instead of just telling stories like, *There were 5 ducks and 2 more came. How many ducks are there?* Teachers should ask questions like: *The answer is 5 ducks. What is the question?* Instead of just asking, *What is 3 + 2?* teachers should also say things like *Give me 2 different ways to make 5.* We want students to be reasoning about numbers in a variety of ways, using as many scaffolds as they need to become confident and competent.

Scaffolding

Scaffolds are a fundamental part of guided math lessons. There are so many different types of scaffolds. We are going to discuss grouping scaffolds, language scaffolds and tool scaffolds. Grouping scaffolds help students to become proficient by having students work with partners and in small groups, before they practice the skill on their own. This is the social aspect of grappling with the content. Oftentimes, students learn a great deal from each other through discussions and interactions. In the group, you can partner the students up and watch them play the game and take notes and ask different questions to guide them as they work together.

Language is often scaffolded with illustrated pictures of the vocabulary and language stems on sentence strips. Dixon (2018b) talks about how in the beginning of learning about a concept that it can be productive for students to have to explain the topic without the "cover" of the vocabulary. Meaning that sometimes students will use words but not understand the concepts, but their lack of understanding can be hidden by the use of the correct vocabulary. If they don't have that, then they have to explain the math. In later lessons, when students understand the math, then it's ok to upfront the vocabulary.

Scaffolding is so important and yet we have to be really careful not to overscaffold and as Dixon warns to also avoid "just in case" scaffolding (2018c). We want to help students as they need it, but we do not want to steal the struggle. Students need the opportunity to engage in the productive struggle, but it should not be an unproductive struggle (Hiebert & Grouws, 2007; Blackburn, 2018). There is a very careful balancing act that teachers conduct when scaffolding in a guided math group.

In the guided math group, teachers should make sure that tools are part of the learning cycle. In planning to unpack the concepts and skills in small groups, teachers should think about the ways in which students can wrestle with topics concretely, pictorially and abstractly. There should also be an emphasis on verbalization and contextualization (NCTM, 2014). The magic of the manipulatives is the conversation and the activities that are done along with them. Students need to reflect on and explain the concepts and how the manipulatives are being used to model those concepts. In a small group, students should be doing the math and exploring and discussing the ideas as they use the manipulatives (Ball, 1992; Baroody, 1989; Bruner, 1960; Burns, n.d.)

Engagement

Engagement is important. Research links engagement to students' *affect*—their feelings and emotions about learning (Mcleod, 1992 cited in Ingram). We find that students' engagement is shaped around the sociocultural environment in which they are learning. How they are constructing knowledge together through discussions, activities and the norms of learning (Op 't Eynde, 2004; Boaler & Greeno, 2000; Greeno, Collins, & Resnick, 1996). The interactions that students have in small guided math groups is very important. It helps to shape students' mathematical identities—who and what they see themselves as in terms of a mathematician.

We find that students are engaged when they participate in strong lessons in a strong community. A strong lesson has a clear purpose, is relevant and makes sense to their lives; it is brain-friendly and flows easily allowing them to quickly get into a "good 'work-flow,'" and dive deep into the material (Claflin, 2014). The strong community of learners in essence means that "they got each other's back!" Everybody is in it to win it with each other. Students are helpful, trusting, risk-taking and comfortable. In the small group, they should be willing to try things out and assured that it is not always going to work the first time and that they might not get it even the second time around but that with perseverance they can learn it.

Another really important aspect of working with small children is the wonder of learning. The guided math table is a special experience. I like to have guided math journals and special pencils and toolkits for students to work with at the table. Students look forward to coming to the guided math group. Often, I use dice, dominos, cards and board games. Since the same structure can be used, the students are ready to work on the content. Meaning, if we play bingo, then students know that structure, so they can immediately focus on the content. I might play a lower doubles bingo game with one group and a make 10 bingo game with another group.

Student Accountability

While the students are working in math workstations, they should be filling out different sheets of the work they are doing (see Figures 2.6, 2.7 and 2.8). They should be recording what they are doing. Some sheets record everything that students are doing. Other games have students record only some of their work.

The most important thing about a math workshop is that you organize it well from the beginning. You must do the first 20 days. In the first 20 days you teach the students how to work in the workshop. Here is a resource for that: www.drnickinewton.com/downloads/

Students have to learn how to work independently before you start pulling them in to guided math groups. The premise of math workshop is that all students can work on their own productively, before you start working with them in small groups.

There are two key elements to a good workstation. The first is a clear goal for the workstation. Students need to know what the math is and how they are going to work on that math and what it looks like when they are actually learning that math. The second is that they have an accountability system so that they know the teacher will be monitoring their work.

Figure 2.6 Example 1: Student Recording Sheet

Comparing Numbers	
Roll the dice. Record your roll. Circle the bigger number. Whoever has the largest number wins a point. Whoever gets 5 points first wins the round. Whoever wins three rounds wins the game.	
Partner 1	**Partner 2**

Figure 2.7 Example 2: Student Recording Sheet

Recording Sheet: Top It

I had 3 + 2 which made 5. My partner had 4 + 5 which made 9. My partner had more because 9 is more than 5.

1	2	3	4	5	6	7	8	9	10	11	12	13	14	15	16	17	18	19	20

_____ is greater than _____.

_____ is less than _____.

_____ is the same as _____.

Figure 2.8 Example 3: Student Recording Sheet

Recording Sheet: Board Game

When I went around the board I solved several doubles facts problems. I can use my doubles to help me

I solved:
3 + 3 = 6
2 + 2 = 4
1 + 1 = 2

Key Points

◆ Assessment
◆ Grouping
◆ Differentiation
◆ Rotations
◆ Standards-based
◆ Depth of Knowledge
◆ Scaffolding
◆ Engagement
◆ Student accountability

Chapter Summary

The key to great guided math groups is assessment. When you have great assessments, then you can group appropriately for differentiation that matters. Lessons should be standards-based. Teachers must always plan for the level of rigor in the lesson. Lessons should be scaffolded with language supports, tools, templates and student grouping. All the other students must be accountable to the work they are doing in the workstations. Engagement is necessary.

Reflection Questions

1. What specific assessments do you have around the priority standards?
2. In what ways are you evaluating your lessons for rigor?
3. In what ways are you scaffolding lessons?
4. How do you know that the other students are on task and learning in the math workstation?

References

Ball, D. L. (1992). Magical Hopes: Manipulatives and the Reform of Math Education. *American Educator: The Professional Journal of the American Federation of Teachers*, 16(2), 14–18, 46–47.

Baroody, A. J. (1989). Manipulatives Don't Come with Guarantees. *Arithmetic Teacher*, 37(2), 4–5.

Blackburn, B. (2018). Retrieved January 5, 2020 from www.ascd.org/ascd-express/vol14/num11/productive-struggle-is-a-learners-sweet-spot.aspx

Boaler, J., & Greeno, J. G. (2000). Identity, Agency, and Knowing in Mathematical Worlds. In J. Boaler (Ed.), *Multiple Perspectives on Mathematics Teaching and Learning* (pp. 171–200). Westport, CT: Ablex Publishing.

Bruner, J. S. (1960). On Learning Mathematics. *The Mathematics Teacher*, 53(8), 610–619.

Burns, M. (n.d.). *How to Make the Most of Manipulatives*. Retrieved August 28, 2016 from http://teacher.scholastic.com/lessonrepro/lessonplans/instructor/burns.htm?nt_id=4&url=http://store.scholastic.com/Books/Hardcovers/Harry-Potter-and-the-Chamber-of-SecretsThe-Illustrated-Edition-Book-2?eml=SSO/aff/20160429/21181/banner/EE/affiliate/////2-247765/&affiliate_id=21181&click_id=1707726852

Claflin, P. (2014). Retrieved January 20, 2020 from www.theanswerisyes.org/2014/12/08/student-engagement-checklist/

Dixon. (2018a). Retrieved January 4, 2020 from www.dnamath.com/blog-post/five-ways-we-undermine-efforts-to-increase-student-achievement-and-what-to-do-about-it/

Dixon. (2018b). Retrieved January 4, 2020 from www.dnamath.com/blog-post/five-ways-we-undermine-efforts-to-increase-student-achievement-and-what-to-do-about-it-part-4-of-5/

Dixon. (2018c). Retrieved January 4, 2020 from www.dnamath.com/blog-post/five-ways-we-undermine-efforts-to-increase-student-achievement-and-what-to-do-about-it-part-3-of-5/

Greeno, J. G., Collins, A. M., & Resnick, L. B. (1996). Cognition and Learning. In D. C. Berliner & R. C. Calfee (Eds.), *Handbook of Educational Psychology* (pp. 15–46). London: Prentice Hall International.

Hiebert, J., & Grouws, D. A. (2007). The Effects of Classroom Mathematics Teaching on Students' Learning. In F. K. Lester Jr. (Ed.), *Second Handbook of Research on Mathematics Teaching and Learning* (pp. 371–404). Charlotte, NC: Information Age.

McLeod, D. B. (1992). Research on Affect in Mathematics Education: A Reconceptualization. In D. Grouws (Ed.), *Handbook of Research on Mathematics Teaching and Learning* (pp. 575–596). New York: NCTM and Macmillan.

National Council of Teachers of Mathematics. (2014). *Principles to Actions: Ensuring Mathematical Success for All*. Reston, VA: National Council of Teachers of Mathematics.

Op 't Eynde, P. (2004). A Socio-constructivist Perspective on the Study of Affect in Mathematics Education. In M. J. Hoines & A. B. Fuglestad (Eds.), *28th Conference of the International Group for the Psychology of Mathematics Education* (Vol. 1, pp. 118–122). Bergen, Norway: Bergen University College.

Owocki, G., & Goodman, Y. M. (2002). *Kidwatching: Documenting Children's Literacy Development*. Portsmouth, NH: Heinemann.

Richardson, K. (n.d.). Retrieved January 17, 2020 from http://assessingmathconcepts.com/

Shafer, L. (2016). *Summer Math Loss. Why Kids Lose Math Knowledge, and How Families Can Work to Counteract It*. Retrieved January 15, 2019 from www.gse.harvard.edu/news/uk/16/06/summer-math-loss

3

Architecture of a Small Group Lesson

Guided math groups can look many different ways. Sometimes they are more of an exploration of a concept with manipulatives like ten frames and counters, while othertimes they are practicing a skill in the form of a dice game. The elements of the guided math lesson are the same, but the sequencing can be different. For example, you might start with an energizer and then review a skill and play a game to practice that skill. On the other hand, you might be exploring decompositions of a number with Cuisenaire rods first and then afterwards discuss what the math you were exploring was about.

Here is an example of the sequence of a lesson (see Figure 3.1):

Figure 3.1 Example of the Structure of the Lesson

Introduction

Agenda

- ♦ *I am* learning to/*I can*
- ♦ Vocabulary/language frames
- ♦ Launch by teacher
- ♦ Student activity (alone/pairs/group)
- ♦ Wrap-up/reflection
- ♦ Next steps

Every small group lesson should begin with some form of an introduction to the lesson. In this introduction, students will often go over the agenda (Figure 3.2). The teacher can write it up as an agenda so students know what the general outline of the lesson is and what they will be doing. At some point in the lesson, depending on the type of lesson, the teacher would then go over the "*I am* learning to" statement as well as what it looks like when students can actually do that skill or understand that concept.

After that is discussed, the group might talk about the math vocabulary and phrases that are associated with the current topic, if they are already familiar with the words. This is very important because everyone will use this vocabulary throughout the lesson. However, sometimes the vocabulary is discussed at the end of the lesson (see Dixon, 2018). In this case, the students talk about what they were doing and name it with math words.

Then, the lesson begins with either a discussion, an exploration or an activity. The teacher might model it or might just jump into the topic. Oftentimes, the teacher will ask the students to give their input about the topic before they begin. After a time of exploration, the students will begin to further explore the topic, either on their own, with a partner or with the whole small group.

DOI: 10.4324/9781003169529-3

Figure 3.2 Agenda Example

Agenda

We are learning to SUBTRACT!

4 − 2 = ?

Talk about it

Play a game: Smash it!

Talk about it some more....

At the end, the teacher will lead the debrief. This is where the students will discuss what the math was for the day, as well as how they practiced that math. They should also talk about how they feel they are doing with that math. This is the part of the lesson where students are reflecting and monitoring their process. They talk about the parts of the topic that are "easy-peasy" and the parts that are "tricky." Language is important, so instead of saying difficult or hard, I tend to say "tricky, fuzzy or climbing." You can ask the students do they get it, do they kind of get it or do they not get it yet.

Planning

Planning is key (see Figures 3.3 through 3.7). As you are planning for the guided math lesson, it is important to think about the differences between the content, the context and the activity. The content could be to teach students how to compose 10. The context could be a story about finding ways to make 10. The activity could be to play a card game where they have to make tens. This comes up when mapping math content. There is a difference between an activity and a skill. An activity is to actually do something, like play a doubles board game. The skill is the verb—to be able to double a number. The teacher should be planning success criteria for both the product and the process. An example of the content criteria (see Figure 3.3):

Figure 3.3 Success Criteria Chart

I am going to *play a make 5 game.*
So that I can *practice make 5 facts.*
I will know that I can do it *when I can make 5 from any number from 0 to 5 using mental math.*

An example of process criteria is to think about what practices you want students to be able to do:

♦ I can *explain* how to make 5 with any number.
♦ I can *model* a make 5 fact.

Clarke states that when we define process success criteria for students, it helps them do these six things:

1. Ensure appropriate focus
2. Provide opportunity to clarify their understanding
3. Identify success for themselves
4. Begin to identify where the difficulties lie
5. Discuss how they will improve
6. Monitor their own progress

(cited in Dyer, n.d.)

In the guided math group, everyone should know what the criteria is and should discuss it. Dyer notes that it is important for students to think about the "How will we know?" question. When students wrestle with this question they begin "to understand the learning behind the learning target."

This enables students to better understand what teachers expect them to know, understand, or be able to do, as well as what constitutes a proficient performance. This allows students to support each other and take responsibility for their own learning by helping them accurately and appropriately evaluate learning against shared expectations and make any necessary adjustments to the learning. Students become activated as learners.

(n.d.)

Think about this in terms of your guided math lessons. Do the students understand the success criteria? Do they know what they are expected to know, understand and be able to do? What are you looking for in the products or performances to know that the students were successful? How will you judge if it was successful? What will you use to judge the effectiveness of the product or performance? What counts as successful?

If the objective is for students to learn different efficient flexible strategies for adding, then the success criteria might be that:

◆ Students' explanations include the names of the strategies.
◆ Students can discuss different ways to think about the same problem.
◆ In the explanations, students include a clear description of what they did (they can verbalize the strategy).
◆ Students can model their thinking.

You could also have this discussion at the end of the lesson, after students have explored many different strategies. You could then talk about what it means to be flexible and efficient. You could have a checklist or rubric that has the criteria on it.

In the guided math group, the goal is for both teacher and students to be questioning. The expected answers should require thinking, not just a quick yes or no. Students should be thinking and explaining the work. Guided math should not be show and tell. It should be teachers spring boarding students into mathematical thinking. The guided math group is a space for the "having of very good ideas" by all. In the guided math group the students should be taking the responsibility for learning and reflecting on their learning, as well as evaluating themselves and others. They should not be passive listeners or just "yes men and women." They should be active participants in the construction of rich mathematical ideas. To make this happen, there must be a great deal of planning.

Planning and Preparation

There are many different planning templates but they basically all have the same information. When planning it is important to think about the big idea, the enduring understanding, the essential question, the *I am learning to* statement, the assessments and possibly on the same template or a different one, the workstations or menu activities. See the list of the templates below (Figures 3.4–3.13).

Figure 3.4 Quick Plan

Week:	Assessments	Workstations
Big Idea:	Entrance Slips:	Group 1
Enduring Understanding:	Exit Slips:	Group 2
Essential Question		Group 3
I am learning to . . .		Group 4

Figure 3.5 Guided Math Planning Template

Unit of Study: Big Idea: Enduring Understanding: Standard:			Essential Question: Vocabulary: Language Frame: I Can Statement:	
	Group 1:	Group 2:	Group 3:	Group 4:
Monday	Lesson: Materials: DOK Level: Concrete/Pictorial/Abstract	Lesson: Materials: DOK Level: Concrete/Pictorial/Abstract	Lesson: Materials: DOK Level: Concrete/Pictorial/Abstract	Lesson: Materials: DOK Level: Concrete/Pictorial/Abstract
Tuesday	Lesson: Materials: DOK Level: Concrete/Pictorial/Abstract	Lesson: Materials: DOK Level: Concrete/Pictorial/Abstract	Lesson: Materials: DOK Level: Concrete/Pictorial/Abstract	Lesson: Materials: DOK Level: Concrete/Pictorial/Abstract
Wednesday	Lesson: Materials: DOK Level: Concrete/Pictorial/Abstract	Lesson: Materials: DOK Level: Concrete/Pictorial/Abstract	Lesson: Materials: DOK Level: Concrete/Pictorial/Abstract	Lesson: Materials: DOK Level: Concrete/Pictorial/Abstract
Thursday	Lesson: Materials: DOK Level: Concrete/Pictorial/Abstract	Lesson: Materials: DOK Level: Concrete/Pictorial/Abstract	Lesson: Materials: DOK Level: Concrete/Pictorial/Abstract	Lesson: Materials: DOK Level: Concrete/Pictorial/Abstract
Friday	Lesson: Materials: DOK Level: Concrete/Pictorial/Abstract	Lesson: Materials: DOK Level: Concrete/Pictorial/Abstract	Lesson: Materials: DOK Level: Concrete/Pictorial/Abstract	Lesson: Materials: DOK Level: Concrete/Pictorial/Abstract

Figure 3.6 Guided Math Planning Template

Guided Math Groups	
Big Ideas: Enduring Understandings: Essential Questions: Vocabulary: Language Frames:	Cycle of Engagement: Concrete, Pictorial, Abstract Depth of Knowledge Level: 1 2 3 4 Standard/I can statement:
Group 1: Novice Students:	Group 2: Apprentice Students:
Group 3: Practitioner Students:	Group 4: Expert Students:

Figure 3.7 Guided Math Template 3

Guided Math Lesson Plan: Group:		
Week: Big Idea: Enduring Understanding:	Standard: *I Can/I Am* Learning To Statement:	Vocabulary: Language Frame: Materials:
Lesson: Intro: Guided Practice: Individual Practice: Sharing: Debrief:		
Comments/Notes: Next Steps:		

Figure 3.8 Guided Math Planning Template

Guided Math Lesson		
Big Ideas: Enduring Understandings: Essential Questions:	Vocabulary: Language Frame:	Standard: *I can/I am* learning to . . . Concrete/Pictorial/Abstract
DOK Level: 1 2 3 4	Goal: ♦ Remediate ♦ Teach ♦ Dive Deeper	Materials/Tools {table below}

Materials/Tools:

dice	board games	unifix cubes/bears/tiles
dominos	counters	base ten blocks
deck of cards	calculators	pattern blocks
white boards/ markers	gm journals	geoboards

Beginning of the Lesson	Guided Practice	Independent Practice
Assessment/Exit Slip	Discussion	Questions

Comments/Notes: Aha: Wow: Rethink: Next Moves:

Figure 3.9 Guided Math Planning Template

Guided Math		
Group: **Week:**		
Big Idea: Enduring Understandings: Essential Questions:	Vocabulary: Language Frame: DOK Level: 1 2 3 4	Lessons: 1st 2nd 3rd
Content Questions:		
Name	What I Noticed	Next Steps

Figure 3.10 Guided Math Planning Template

Guided Math Template	
Big Idea: Enduring Understanding: Essential Question: I Can Statement:	Materials
Cycle of Engagement Concrete: Pictorial: Abstract	**Vocabulary & Language Frames** Vocabulary: Talk Frame:
	Other notes;

Figure 3.11 Differentiated Lesson Planner

Three Differentiated Lessons		
Emerging	On Grade Level	Above Grade Level

WATCH OUT Misunderstandings and Misconceptions

Figure 3.12 Differentiated Planning Template

Group 1: Emergent	Group 2: Early Fluent	Group 3: Fluent	Group 4: Advanced Fluent

WATCH OUT Misunderstandings and Misconceptions

Figure 3.13 Guided Math Planning Template

Guided Math Planning Sheet	
Launch	
Model	
Checking for Understanding	
Guided Practice/Checking for Understanding	
Set up for Independent Practice	

Key Points

- Architecture of the lesson
  - *I am* learning to/*I can*
  - Vocabulary/language frames
  - Launch by teacher
  - Student activity (alone/pairs/group)
  - Wrap-up
  - Next steps

- Planning template
- Discussion throughout

Chapter Summary

There is a suggested architecture for small guided math groups. Teachers must plan for the learning goal, the vocabulary supports, the tools, the launch of the lesson, the students practicing the math, the wrap-up, the reflection and the next steps. All of these elements are an important part of the lesson. They all contribute to the success of the guided math group. Using planning templates with these elements on them helps teachers to plan for each of the elements.

Reflection Questions

1. Do your guided math lessons have all of the elements in them?
2. What types of templates are you currently using for guided math groups?
3. What is an element that you need to focus on in the architecture?

References

Dixon, J. (2018). *Small Group Instruction {from the (Un)Productive Practices Series}*. Five Ways We Undermine Efforts to Increase Student Achievement (and What To Do About It).
   Blog Post 4: www.dnamath.com/blog-post/five-ways-we-undermine-efforts-to-increase-student-achievement-and-what-to-do-about-it-part-4-of-5/

Dyer, K. (n.d.). Retrieved January 20, 2020 from www.nwea.org/blog/2018/what-you-need-to-know-when-establishing-success-criteria-in-the-classroom/

4

Talk in the Guided Math Group

One of the most important things that happen in the guided math group is the discussion. We have to teach students to be active participants and engaged listeners. We want them to respect each other deeply and seek to truly understand each other without judgment. They have to learn to develop and defend their thinking, justify their answers and respectfully disagree with each other. The National Council of Teachers of Mathematics (NCTM) defines math talk as "the ways of representing, thinking, talking, and agreeing and disagreeing that teachers and students use to engage in [mathematical] tasks" (NCTM, 1991).

Questions

It is so important to ask good questions. The questions should reach beyond the answer. As Phil Daro notes, we have to go "beyond answer-getting" (https://vimeo.com/79916037). The questions in the guided math group should be designed to get students to understand more fundamentally the mathematics of the grade level. Good questions don't just happen, they are planned for. The teacher should know ahead of time the types of questions that she will ask and why she will ask them. In the plan for the lesson, the teacher should brainstorm some possible questions that push student thinking. These are not yes or no questions, but rather ones that require students to explain themselves, show what they know, and defend and justify their thinking (see Figure 4.1).

When students are sitting in that group, they should be having an engaging experience that builds mathematical knowledge and skills. At the table, students should be encouraged to actively participate. They should be thinking out loud, sharing their thoughts, respectively analyzing and critiquing the thoughts and actions of others, and taking risks throughout the explorations. We should always be thinking about the levels of rigor of the conversation that the students are engaged in (see Figure 4.2).

It is very important to include *Open Questions* as part of your repertoire at the guided math table. Here is an example: *The answer is 12 elephants. What is the question?* Although you will ask some questions that require students to remember a fact or show you that they can do a skill, your questions must extend beyond this level. You should be focusing on questions that have more than one answer or way of solving the problem.

Questions That Pique Curiosity

Your questions should pique curiosity. They should lead students into further explorations. They don't have to be answered immediately. Students should have a sense of wonder. There should be some "Aha" moments, some "Wow" moments and some "I don't get it" moments.

For example, "What if we didn't have addition?" "Tell me three situations in which you would use subtraction." "Why is multiplication important in real life?"

DOI: 10.4324/9781003169529-4

Figure 4.1 Planning for Great Questions

Before the Lesson	During the Lesson	After the Lesson
Plan what you want to get your students to think about. The tasks that you choose will determine the thinking that occurs.	**Observe, monitor and note what is happening in the group. Checklists, Post-its and anecdotal note structures work well here.**	**Reflect, assess and decide what's next.**
How will you go about asking questions? Will it be an open discussion?	What is your data collection system during the lesson?	What did you see?
What questions will you ask them?	How will you scaffold student questioning?	What did you hear?
		What did the students do?
How will you set them up to actively listen and productively participate?	How will you scaffold student to student interactions?	What do you need to do next?
How will you get them to engage with the ideas of others?		What instructional moves will you make?
How will you get them to offer detailed explanations of their own thinking using numbers, words and model?		What pedagogical moves will you make?
Plan for misconceptions. How will you address them and redirect students?		

Figure 4.2 Depth of Knowledge In terms of rigor there are four levels of questions.

DOK 1 At this level students are recalling facts and knowledge.	DOK 2 At this level students explain their thinking.	DOK 3 At this level students have to justify, defend and prove their thinking with objects, drawings and diagrams.
What is the answer to ??? Can you model the problem? Can you identify the answer that matches this equation?	How do you know that the equation is correct? Can you pick the correct answer and explain why it is correct? How can you model that problem in more than one way? What is another way to model that problem? Can you model that on the. . . . ??? Give me an example of a . . . type of problem. Which answer is incorrect? Explain your thinking.	Can you prove that your answer is correct? Prove that . . . Explain why that is the answer. Show me how to solve that and explain what you are doing.

*Level 4 is more strategic project-based thinking questions.

Student to Student Conversations

It is crucial that the teacher sets up a discussion where students are asking each other questions. They could have question rings, bookmarks, mini-anchor charts or other scaffolds to help them ask each other questions (see Figures 4.3–4.5). In kindergarten you could have one to three questions that you teach students to ask over time. They could be up on a chart. In these conversations one of the things that students are doing is listening to each other and comparing what they did.

Probing Questions

Teacher questions as well as student to student questions should provide insight into student thinking. During the guided math lesson and after it, the teacher should jot down what they have learned about student thinking, student knowledge and how they are making sense of the math they are learning.

Figure 4.3 Question Bookmark

Question Bookmark
Questions we could ask each other:
How do you know?
Are you sure about that?
What is another way to do that?
Why did you use that model?
Can you explain your thinking?

Figure 4.4 Talk Cards/Talk Ring

I agree because...	I disagree because..	I need some time to think.	Why is that true?

Are you sure?	Do you agree or disagree?	Can you think of another way?	I'm confused still..
Yes I'm sure because No, I'm not sure. I'm thinking about it.	or	Way 1 Way 2	

Figure 4.5 5 Talk Moves Poster

5 talk moves poster				
Revoice	Restate	Reason	Wait Time	Group participation
I heard you say…	*Who can say what she said in your own words?*	*Are you sure? Can you prove it?*	*Give me a few seconds*	*Who wants to add to that?*

Source: Chapin, O'Connor, and Anderson (2009).

Scaffolding Questions for ELLs

Students should understand the questions being asked. The language should be accessible, and everyone should have a way to enter into the conversation. When thinking about instruction with English Language Learners, we must consider the type of language support they will need (https://mathsolutions.com/math-talk/; http://fspsscience.pbworks.com/w/file/fetch/80214878/Leveled_20Questions_20for_20ELLs; www.aworldoflanguagelearners.com/asking-answering-questions-with-ells/). Oftentimes, they will need help with syntax and sentence structure, so it is important to scaffold these into the conversation. Give students an opportunity to refer to language stems, use language bookmarks, write down and/or draw the answer (see Figure 4.6).

Figure 4.6 ELL Questions

Low Levels of Support: (advanced language learners) (levels 3 & 4)	Moderate Levels of Support: (developing language learners) (level 2)	High Levels of Support: (emerging language learners) (level 1)
Use a word bank (illustrated)	Use a sentence frame	Allow students to draw/write the answer
Explain how s/he did that	I got the answer by _____.	Point to the . . .
Explain your thinking	How can you use ____ to help you solve _____?	Show me your answer
Explain your model/strategy	How can you model that?	Which is the best answer?
What are two ways you could model your thinking?	What is the name of that strategy? (mini-anchor chart)	What is the name of that strategy? Do you see it here? (mini-anchor chart of strategies)
Can you describe your thinking?	How did you do that?	Give students a model sentence and a sentence frame
Can you show us what you did?	Why did you use that model/strategy?	
Can you describe how you did it?	How did s/he do that?	How did you get the answer?
Can you explain what s/he did?	Is it this or that?	How did you _____?
Why is that true?	Which strategy did you use? (visual support)	Do you agree? Yes or no?
Why is that not true?		Show me the _____
Explain how you did it		Point to the _____
Decide if s/he is correct		Circle the ____
		Can you point to the strategy you used?

Source: Adapted from http://fspsscience.pbworks.com/w/file/fetch/80214878/Leveled_20Questions_20for_20ELLs
www.aworldoflanguagelearners.com/asking-answering-questions-with-ells/

Although these are structures for ELLs, they are great question types to consider with the various students you are working with. They are also great ways to think about scaffolding questions for special education students.

5 Talk Moves and More

The idea of having a framework for how students engage with each other is very important. Chapin, O'Connor, and Anderson (2009) theorized this framework around 5 talk moves, revoicing, restating, wait time, group participation and reasoning. There are also other really helpful frameworks (Kazem & Hintz, 2014; O'Connell & O'Connor, 2007). In the next section we will explore how some of these can help us structure the discussions in guided math groups. Oftentimes, these structures are used together; for example a teacher might ask someone to restate what someone said and then encourage the group to add on (see Figures 4.7–4.16).

Figure 4.7 Revoicing

What it is	What it does	What it sounds like
The teacher restates in the words of the student what they just said.	This allows the student to hear back what they said, the other students to hear and process what has been said and everyone to think about it and make sure they understand it. This teaches students the power of hearing what they have said and trying to make sense of it.	*So you said. . . . Is that correct? Let me make sure I understand, you are saying. . . .* *So first you . . . and then you . . .* *So you used this model?* *So you used this strategy?*

Figure 4.8 Restating

What it is	What it does	What it sounds like
The teacher or other students restate in their own words what has been said. Then, they verify that restating with the original student.	This allows the student to hear back what they said, the other students to hear and process what has been said and everyone to think about it and make sure they understand it. This requires that students listen and pay attention to each other so they can restate what has been said. This teaches students how to listen to each other and make sense of what their peers are saying.	*Who can restate what Susie just said?* *Who can tell in their own words what Jamal just said?* *Who can explain what Carol meant when she said . . . ?*

Figure 4.9 Wait Time

What it is	What it does	What it sounds like
Teachers and students give each other 20–30 seconds of uninterrupted time to think, write or draw about what they are doing. This is done after the question is asked and then also when the answer is given. Students should be given the time to think about the answer and then respond to it.	This allows students the time to gather their thoughts, clarify their thinking for themselves and just time to think. It gives more people time to process what is happening. It teaches them the power of stopping to think instead of rushing into a conversation.	*Ok, now I am going to ask some questions, but I want you to take some think time before you answer.* *Terri just gave an answer. Let's think about what she just said before we respond.* *Show me with a silent hand signal when you are ready.* *Let's give everyone some time to think about this . . .* *Is everybody ready to share or do you need more time? Show me with a hand signal.*

Figure 4.10 Reasoning

What it is	What it does	What it sounds like
Teachers and students are asking each other for evidence and proof to defend and justify what they are saying.	This requires students to engage with each other's thinking. They must compare, contrast, justify and defend their thinking with the other group members. This teaches students the power of defending and justifying their thinking with evidence and proof.	*Why did you do that?* *Is that true?* *Why did you use that strategy?* *Can you prove it?* *Are you sure?* *How do you know?* *Why did you use that model?* *Does that make sense?* *Do you agree or disagree, and why or why not?* *How is your thinking like Tom's?* *Is there another way?*

Figure 4.11 Group Participation

What it is	What it does	What it sounds like
Students write down or model their thinking and then share it with the whole group.	This allows students to focus on their own strategies and models, jot them down and then share them. This teaches students the power of justifying and defending their thinking.	*Use a model to show . . .* *Illustrate your strategy.* *On your white boards, show us . . .* *In your guided math journal, show your thinking with numbers, words or pictures . . . be ready to share it with the group . . .*

Figure 4.12 Making Connections

What it is	What it does	What it sounds like
Teachers and students are asking each other to make connections with what has been said at the table.	It requires students to listen to each other and think about how what they did connects to what someone else did. This teaches students the power of making connections with each other's thinking.	*How is that the same as what Marta did?* *How is that different from what Joe did?* *This is like what Trini did . . .* *How are these models the same and how are they different?* *How are these strategies the same and how are they different?*

Figure 4.13 Partner Talk

What it is	What it does	What it sounds like
Students talk with their math partners about the math before they share out with the group. They might even draw or write something to share out.	This allows students to think out the math with each other, try to make sense of it and then be able to explain it to the whole group. This teaches students the power of working together to make sense of the math.	*Turn and talk to your partner.* *Tell your partner what you think and why you think that.* *Show and explain to your partner what you did.* *Defend your thinking to your partner.*

Figure 4.14 Prompting Student Participation

What it is	What it does	What it sounds like
The teacher or the students encourage each other to participate in the conversation.	This allows students to participate with each other in the discussion. It openly asks for participation that builds on what has just been said. This teaches students the power of participating in a discussion.	*Who would like to add to that?* *Who wants to say more?* *How did you do it that is the same or different from the way Hong did it?* *Is there another model?* *Is there another strategy?* *Is there another way?*

Figure 4.15 Clarifying One's Thinking

What it is	What it does	What it sounds like
Teachers and students take the time to clarify their thinking.	It allows students to expand on their original thoughts. It requires them to give more examples, show more models and explain at a deeper level.	*Can you explain that further?* *Can you tell us more?* *What does that mean?* *Can you show us a model and explain it?* *Can you illustrate your strategy and explain it?*

Figure 4.16 Reflecting/Revising/Probing

What it is	What it does	What it sounds like
The teacher and the students take time to reflect on what has been said and possibly revise their thinking.	This gives students an opportunity to rethink about what they have just done. They get permission to change their minds. It teaches them the power of reflecting and revising their work.	*Did anybody change their mind?* *Did anybody revise their thinking?* *Now that you see this model, what do you think?* *Now that you see this strategy, what do you think?* *Thinking about what Jamal just said, how does that help us with our thinking?*

It is very important to use different talk moves and structures with students during guided math group in order to scaffold the discussions. The preceding structures can definitely get you started doing this. It is important to plan for what you want to work on so that it isn't just random conversations. You should be explicit with students when teaching these structures. For example, you might say, "Today we are working on wait time. I want you to think about giving each other the time to think as we talk. Remember, just because you are ready, doesn't mean your neighbor is yet."

Key Points

♦ Questions matter
♦ Plan for great questions
♦ DOK questions
♦ Questions that pique curiosity
♦ Student to student conversations
♦ Scaffolding questions for ELLs
♦ 5 talk moves and more

Chapter Summary

We must plan for good conversations. Planning matters. We must think about the ways in which we want our students to engage with each other and then actively do that in our groups. Think about the level of rigor of our questions. Think about what kinds of questions pique curiosity. Consider how we get students to engage with each other respectfully, confidently and competently. We must stay conscious of scaffolding our questions for ELLs so that everyone has a way to enter into the conversations. We need to consider the different types of talk moves that allow us to have rigorous, engaging and productive conversations.

Reflection Questions

1. What stands out for you in this chapter?
2. What will you enact right away?
3. What questions do you still have?

References

Chapin, S., O'Connor, C., & Anderson, N. (2009). *Classroom Discussions: Using Math Talk to Help Students Learn, Grades K-6* (2nd ed.). Sausalito, CA: Math Solutions Publications.

Daro, P. Retrieved December 11, 2020 from https://vimeo.com/79916037

Kazemi, E., & Hintz, A. (2014). *Intentional Talk: How to Structure and Lead Productive Mathematical Discussions*. Portland, ME: Stenhouse.

NCTM. (1991). Professional Standards for Teaching Mathematics. Reston, VA: NCTM.

O'Connell, S., & O'Connor, K. (2007). *Introduction to Communication, Grades 3–5*. Portsmouth, NH: Heinemann.

Retrieved November 24, 2020 from http://fspsscience.pbworks.com/w/file/fetch/80214878/Leveled_20Questions_20for_20ELLs

Retrieved November 24, 2020 from https://mathsolutions.com/math-talk/

Retrieved November 24, 2020 from www.aworldoflanguagelearners.com/asking-answering-questions-with-ells/

5

Small Group Fluency Lessons

Basic fact fluency within 5 in most states and within 10 in others is a major part of fluency in kindergarten. Research says that we should devote at least 10 minutes a day to fluency practice (NCEE, 2009). It should be done as energizers and routines, in workstations and sometimes as guided math lessons. Teachers should integrate fluency work throughout the year because students learn their basic facts at different times.

Fluency is a multi-dimensional concept. We like to think of it as a four-legged stool: accuracy, flexibility, efficiency and instant recall (Brownell & Chazal, 1935; Brownell, 1956/1987; Kilpatrick, Swafford, & Findell, 2001; National Council of Teachers of Mathematics, 2000). Although we eventually want students to have instant recall, we need them to understand what they are doing with the numbers first. The emphasis in the guided math group is to do a variety of engaging, interactive, rigorous and student-friendly activities that build a fundamental understanding of how numbers are in relationship with each other. As you explore the facts with the students, be sure to do concrete, pictorial and abstract activities with them. There should be several ways for students to practice that are fun and challenging. Students should keep track of how they are doing as well.

Research Note

There has been a long debate on traditional fact-based instruction centered around memorization and strategy-based instruction centered around number sense and using strategies. Strategy-based instruction helps students to understand the math they are doing and to do it with eventual flexibility, efficiency, automaticity and accuracy (Baroody, Purpura, Eiland, Reid, & Paliwal, 2016; Henry & Brown, 2008; Thornton, 1978).

◆ Boaler (2015) argues that the emphasis of rote memorization through repetition and timed testing is "unnecessary and damaging."
◆ Several scholars have promoted engaging practice through strategy-based games, and activities can scaffold learning of basic facts (Van de Walle, 2007; Godfrey & Stone, 2013; Bay-Williams & Kling, 2019; Newton, 2016; Newton, Record, & Mello, 2020).

In this chapter we will explore:

◆ Adding within 5
◆ Making 5 facts
◆ Subtracting within 5
◆ Subtracting within 10

DOI: 10.4324/9781003169529-5

Adding Within 5

A note on using story mats: Story mats are really engaging for students. I make all kinds with various scenarios. Students love to play. Story mats tap into that natural inclination to tell stories. When using story mats students tell a story about addition or subtraction. In this lesson, they will be telling stories about adding fish in tanks within 5.

Overview

Figure 5.1 Overview

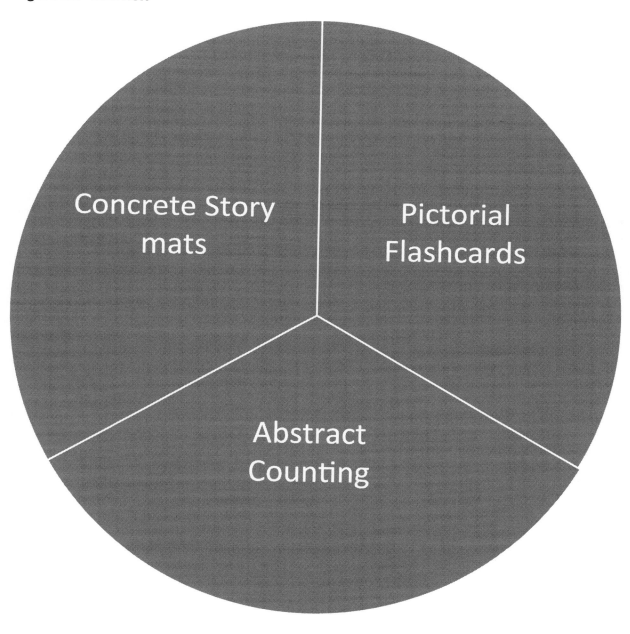

Figure 5.2 Planning Template

Exploring Addition Facts

Big Idea: Addition is joining together.

Enduring Understanding: We can use different strategies to solve addition problems. Counting on from the largest number is an addition strategy.

Essential Question: How can counting on strategies help us to be more efficient?

Content Question: What is counting on?

I can statement: I can add using different strategies.

Materials
- Tools: Rekenrek
- Rekenrek Paper
- Templates: Ten Frame
- Cards
- Crayons

Questions
- What is addition?
- What does it mean to count on?
- Which number do we start with?
- What is the sum?
- What is an addend?

Cycle of Engagement

Concrete: Rekenrek

Pictorial:
Flashcards with numbers and pictures

5 + 1

Vocabulary & Language Frames
- Addition
- Addends
- Sum
- Total
- Strategy
- Model

The sum of ___ and ____ is _____.
___ and ____make _____

Abstract:

5 + 1

Figure 5.3 Differentiation

Three Differentiated Lessons		
In this series of lessons, students are working on the concept of adding using different types of models. They are developing this concept through concrete activities, pictorial activities and abstract activities. Here are some things to think about as you do these lessons.		
Emergent	**On Grade Level**	**Above Grade Level**
Review counting.	Use different models to represent expressions and equations.	Expand the number range.

 Looking for Misunderstandings and Common Errors

When students are first learning to add, some of them are still shaky on counting. So make sure they can count with cardinality before you start adding things together. In the beginning, many students will count all, meaning they will go 1,2 and then 1,2,3 and then 1,2,3,4,5. This is a natural first stage, but we eventually want them to count on from the larger number.

Figure 5.4 Anchor Chart

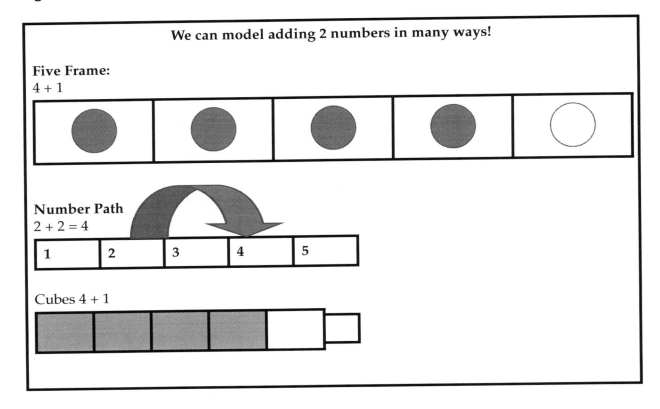

Concrete Lesson

Figure 5.5 Concrete Introduction

Introduction
Concrete Practice

Launch	**Teacher:** Today we are going to work on adding on a story mat. **Vocabulary: adding, model, addend, sum, total** **Math Talk:** _____ and ____ make 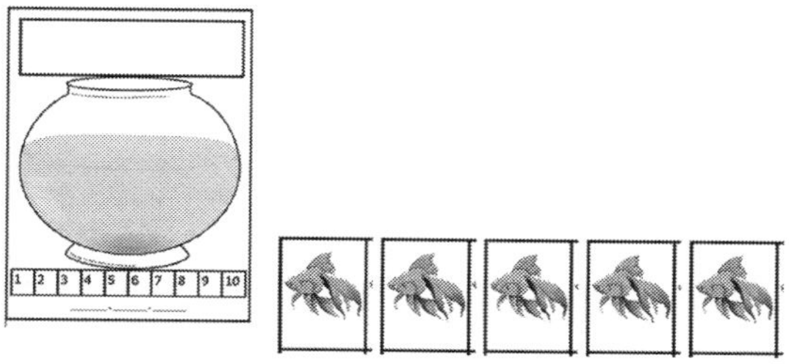 _____. _____ + _____ = _____ Terri had 4  🐟 fish. She got 1 more  🐟. How many does she have now?
Model	**Teacher:** Today we are going to work on adding. Who knows what it means to add? **Jamal:** To put things together. **Teacher:** Yes. Who can give me an example? **Tami:** Like 1 plus 1 is 2. (she shows this on her fingers)
Checking for Understanding	**Teacher:** Excellent example. Who has another one? **Kelli:** Like if we have 2 cubes and we add 2 more. We have like 5, I mean 4. **Teacher:** Great **Teacher:** Ok, smarty pants…. I am going to hand out some story mats and some fish. Each person can tell a story with their counters.

Figure 5.6 Student Activity

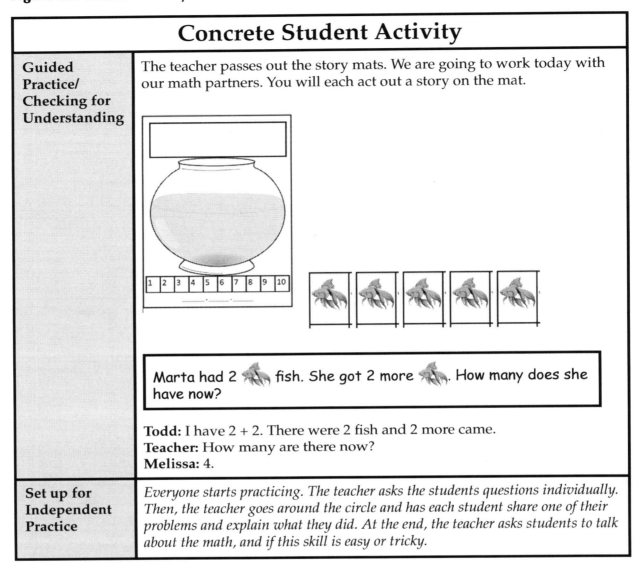

Concrete Student Activity

Guided Practice/ Checking for Understanding	The teacher passes out the story mats. We are going to work today with our math partners. You will each act out a story on the mat.

Marta had 2 fish. She got 2 more. How many does she have now?

Todd: I have 2 + 2. There were 2 fish and 2 more came.
Teacher: How many are there now?
Melissa: 4.

Set up for Independent Practice	*Everyone starts practicing. The teacher asks the students questions individually. Then, the teacher goes around the circle and has each student share one of their problems and explain what they did. At the end, the teacher asks students to talk about the math, and if this skill is easy or tricky.*

Figure 5.7 Lesson Close

Close

- ◆ What did we do today?
- ◆ What was the math we were practicing?
- ◆ What were we doing with the count on strategy?
- ◆ Was this easy or tricky?
- ◆ Turn to a partner and state one thing you learned today.

Visual Lesson

Figure 5.8 Visual Introduction

<table>
<tr>
<td colspan="2" align="center"><h2>Introduction
Exploring with Visual Representations</h2></td>
</tr>
<tr>
<td>Launch</td>
<td>

Teacher: Today we are going to work on adding on a story mat.

Vocabulary: addition, model, addend, sum, total

Math Talk: _____ and _____ make _____. _____ + _____ = _____

</td>
</tr>
<tr>
<td>Model</td>
<td>

Teacher: Today we are going to continue to work on addition. I have these cool flashcards. You are going to count the animals and then tell me how many there are. I am going to give each one of you some flashcards. You will show it to your math partner and tell them the total amount of animals on your card. Then, we are going to go around and you can share some of the cards with the group. Think about how you know you are correct.

Mike turns to Nikeli and says "I see 2 giraffes and 2 zebras. I see 4 animals."

How many animals do you see?

</td>
</tr>
<tr>
<td>Checking for Understanding</td>
<td>

Let's try another one.

Kelli: I see 2 monkeys and 3 zebras. I see 5 animals.

How many animals do you see?

</td>
</tr>
</table>

Figure 5.9 Student Activity

	Visual Student Activity
Guided Practice/ Checking for Understanding	Students work in pairs or triads and explain their thinking to each other. **Teacher:** Tom tell me about your card. **Tom:** I see 3 monkeys and 1 zebra. There are 4 animals. **How many animals do you see?** 
Set up for Independent Practice	*Teacher continues working with individuals and pairs. Everyone also gets a chance to share 1 problem out loud. They wrap up and go to the next workstations.*

Figure 5.10 Lesson Close

Close
◆ What did we do today? ◆ What was the math we were practicing? ◆ What were we doing with our flashcards? ◆ Was this easy or tricky? ◆ Turn to a partner and state one thing you learned today.

Abstract Lesson

Figure 5.11 Abstract Introduction

	Introduction Abstract Exploration
Launch	**Teacher:** Today we are going to continue to work on addition facts. **Vocabulary: addition, model, addend, sum, total** **Math Talk:** _____ and ____ make _____. _____ + _____ = _____
Model	**Teacher:** Today we are going to continue to work on addition facts. Today's game is Biggest Sum! You are going to play with a partner or in a triad. Each person picks a card, calculates the total and then compares the sum. Whoever has the largest sum wins the cards. Whoever has the most cards when all the cards are done, wins the game. **Kate:** I pulled 1 + 1 and that makes 2. **Tami:** I pulled 3 + 1 and that make 4. **Teacher:** Who gets to keep both cards? **Tami:** I do… **Teacher:** Why? **Tami:** Because 4 is more than 2. 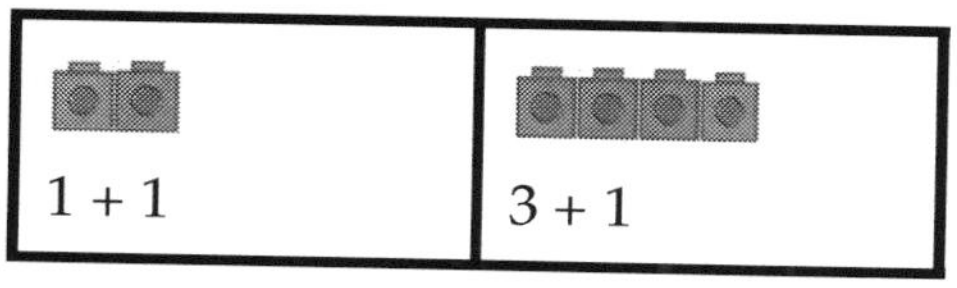
Checking for Understanding	**Teacher:** Who can explain the game? **Mark:** I can. We pull 2 cards. Whoever has the big sum wins! **Teacher:** Ok, any questions? Ok, let's start.

Figure 5.12 Student Activity

	Abstract Student Activity
Guided Practice/ Checking for Understanding	Students work in pairs or triads and explain their thinking to each other. **Teacher:** Tom tell me about your card. **Tom:** I have 4 and 1 and that makes 5. 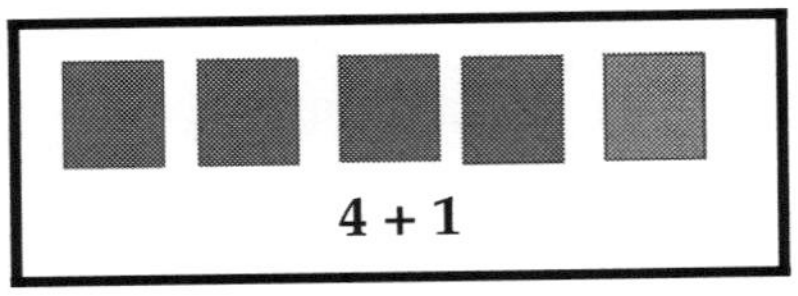 4 + 1 **Kelly:** I have 3 + 1 and that makes 3. **Tom:** That makes 4! **Teacher:** Who is correct? Both of you double check. **Kelly:** Oh yeah, (holding up her fingers, 3 + 1 makes 4). 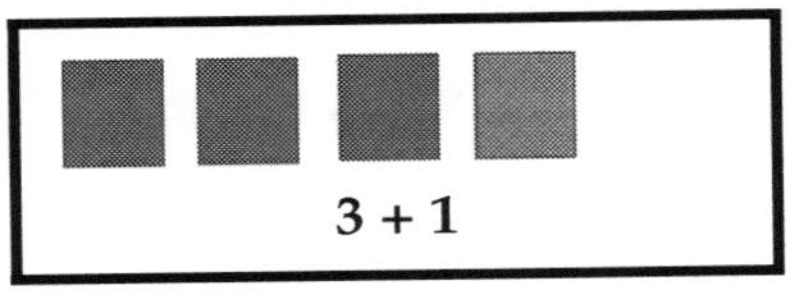 3 + 1
Set up for Independent Practice	*Teacher continues working with individuals and pairs. Everyone also gets a chance to share 1 problem out loud. They wrap up and go to the next workstations.*

Figure 5.13 Lesson Close

Close
◆ What did we do today? ◆ What was the math we were practicing? ◆ Was this easy or tricky? ◆ Turn to a partner and state one thing you learned today.

Figure 5.14 Cube Cards

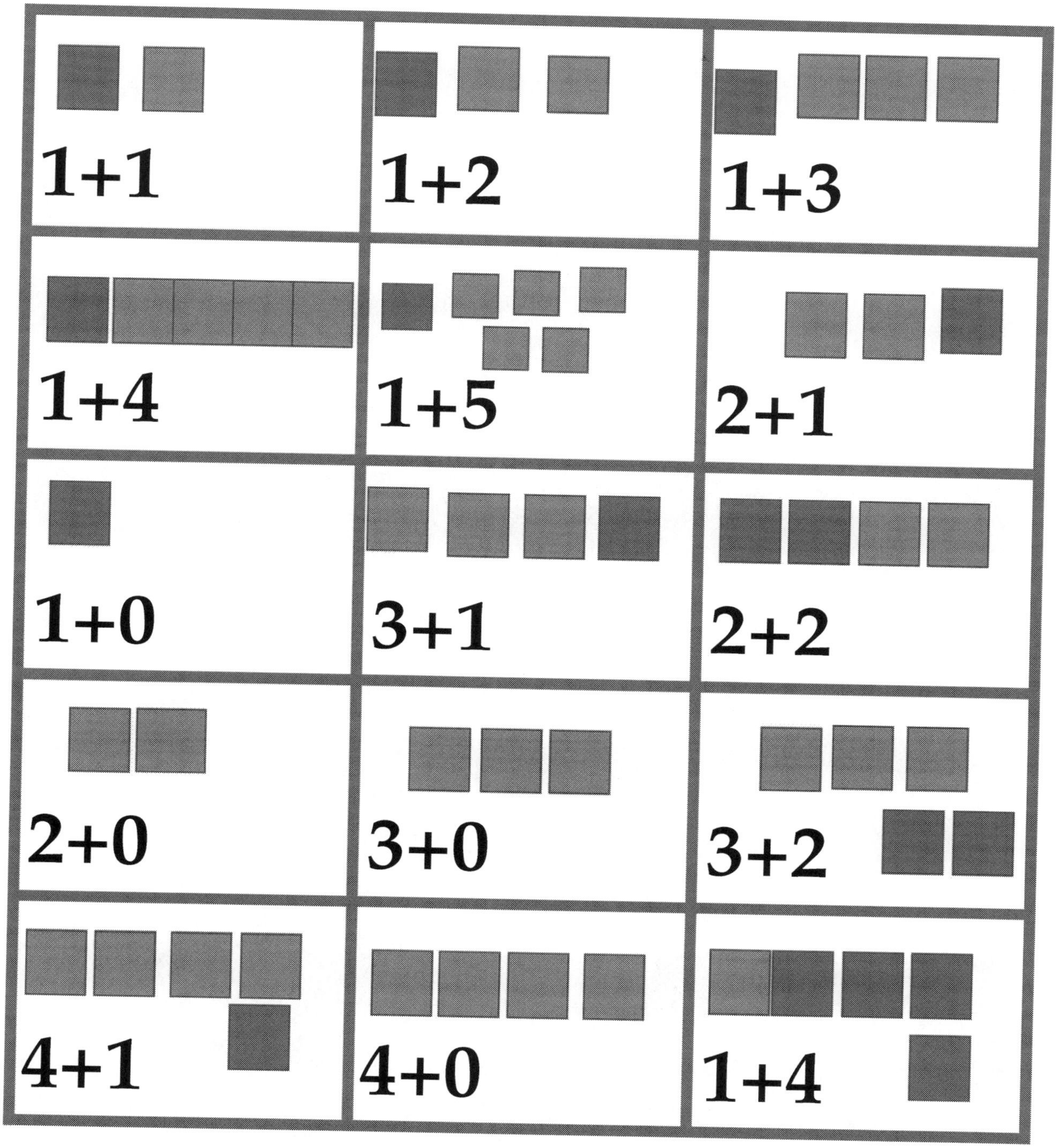

1+1	1+2	1+3
1+4	1+5	2+1
1+0	3+1	2+2
2+0	3+0	3+2
4+1	4+0	1+4

Making 5 Facts

Overview

Figure 5.15 Overview

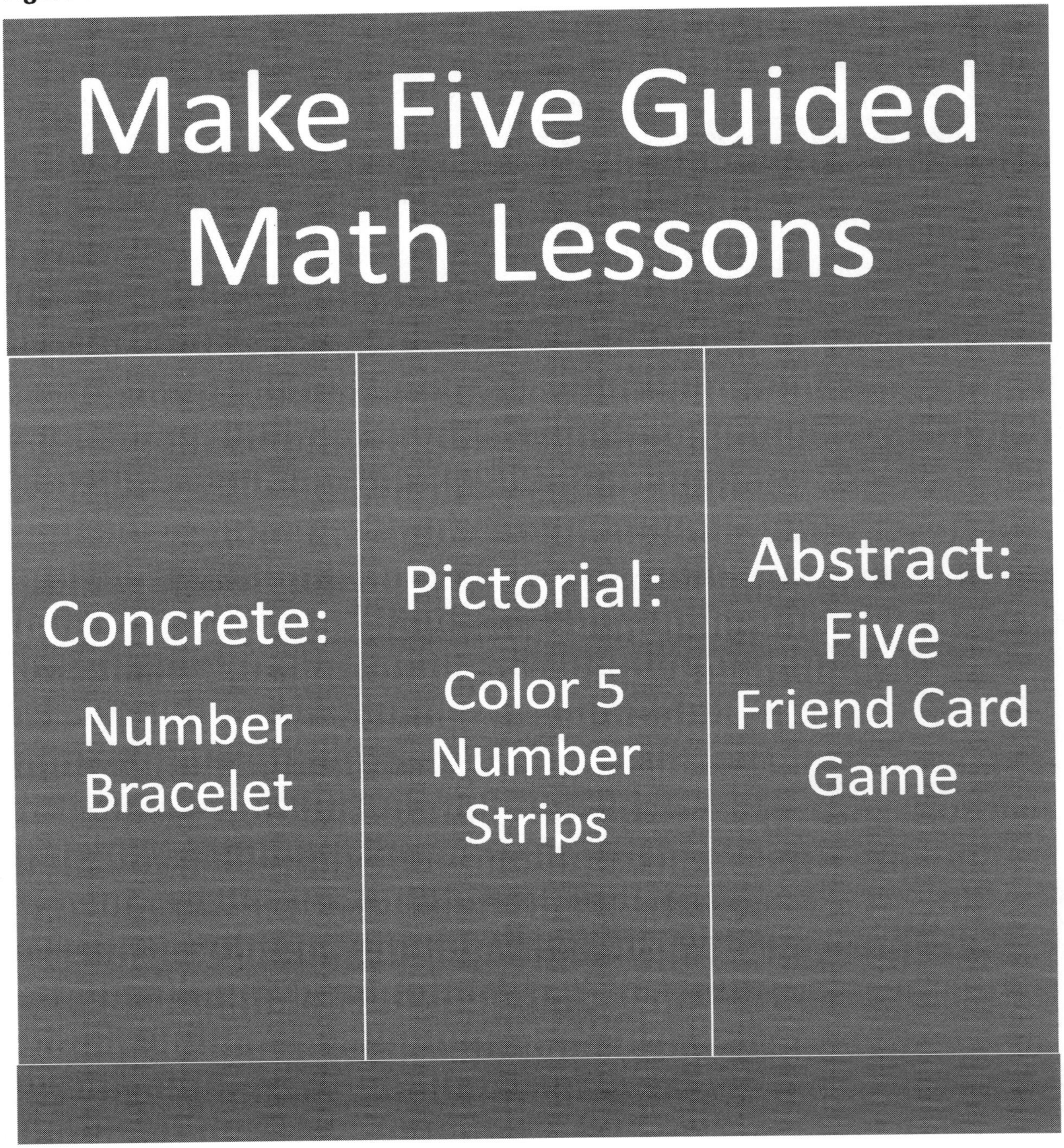
Make Five Guided Math Lessons
Concrete:
Number Bracelet
Pictorial:
Color 5 Number Strips
Abstract:
Five Friend Card Game

Figure 5.16 Planning Template

Combinations of Five

Big Idea: There are certain number combinations that make 5.

Enduring Understanding: Students will understand and be able to recall the number combinations to 5.

Essential Question: What are the ways to make 5?

I can statement: I can make 5 in different ways.

Cycle of Engagement

Concrete: Make 5 Bracelet

Pictorial:

Abstract:: Match Addends and the Sum

4 + 1	5

Materials
- Tools: Cubes
- Templates: Ten Frame
- Cards
- Crayons

Vocabulary & Language Frames

- Addition
- Make Ten
- Addends
- Sum

___ and ___ make _____
The sum of ___ and ____ is _____

Levels of Understanding
- Novice
- Apprentice
- Practitioner
- Expert

Figure 5.17 Differentiation

Three Differentiated Lessons		
In this series of lessons, students are working on the concept of adding to make 5 using different types of models. They are developing this concept through concrete activities, pictorial activities and abstract activities. Here are some things to think about as you do these lessons.		
Emergent	**On Grade Level**	**Above Grade Level**
Review counting.	Use different models to represent expressions and equations.	Expand the number range.

 Looking for Misunderstandings and Common Errors

When students are first learning to add, some of them are still shaky on counting. So make sure they can count with cardinality before you start adding things together. In the beginning, many students will count all, meaning they will go 1,2 and then 1,2,3 and then 1,2,3,4,5. This is a natural first stage, but we eventually want them to count on from the larger number.

Figure 5.18 Anchor Chart

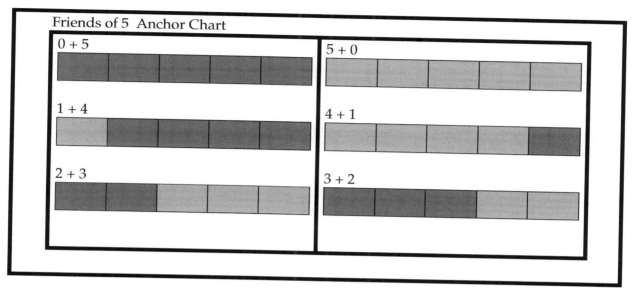

Concrete Lesson

Figure 5.19 Concrete Introduction

Introduction to Concrete Exploration	
Launch	**Teacher:** Today we are going to work on ways to make 5 on our number bracelets. Our goal is to learn different "combinations" of five. **Vocabulary:** combinations, 5, five friends, decompose, compose, separate, break it apart We have an anchor chart here to help us think about 5 friends. The one we made in whole group. **Math Talk:** _____ and _____ make _____. *(Teacher passes out #5 bracelets to every child). Let's look at them. What do you notice? What do you wonder?)* 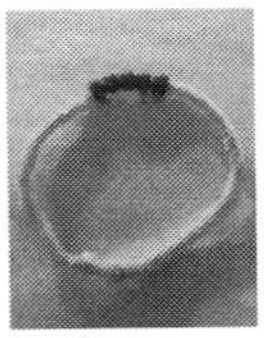
Model	*Students should talk about how there are 5 beads on each bracelet.* **Teacher:** How could we use this to show ways to make 5. **Luke:** We do this with the big hula hoop on the rug. **Teacher:** Yes. So, how could we do this with the little number bracelet? **Luke:** We could separate/ break apart the five into two groups. I could make 1 and 4. 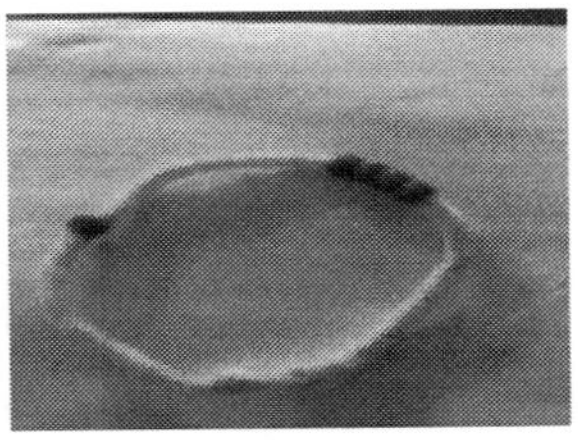
Checking for Understanding	**Teacher:** Now you all are going to each get a number 5 bracelet. We will go around the table and each of you will tell us how you can break it apart. Remember how we talk about it. _____ and _____ make _____.

Figure 5.20 Student Activity

Concrete Student Activity

Guided Practice/ Checking for Understanding	Students go around the table and each of them tell how they broke apart/ separated the number bracelet. You could also scaffold this by giving each student a number card. **Version A: Student gets the number card and breaks the number bracelet into that number and the other part.** **3** **2** and ☐ make 5.  *A more complex version is using the addition sign in an equation.* **Version B: Student gets a card:** **2** + ☐ = 5. 
Set up for Independent Practice	**Teacher:** Who can tell me what the math was today? **Benjamin:** Breaking up numbers on our number bracelets. **Terri:** Like this. I can break my bracelet in 5 on this side and 0 on this side and 5 and 0 make 5. **Teacher:** Yes, when we break up numbers into different parts we are decomposing a number. We are going to keep working with our number bracelets to compose and decompose 5 in our group for a few times. You may go to your workstations now

Figure 5.21 Lesson Close

Close
◆ What did we do today?
◆ What was the math we were practicing?
◆ Was this easy or tricky?
◆ Turn to a partner and state one thing you learned today.

Visual Lesson

Figure 5.22 Visual Introduction

	Introduction to Visual Representations
Launch	**Teacher:** Today we are going to continue to work on drawing our number bracelets. Teacher passes out number bracelet templates. Our goal is to learn different "combinations" to five. **Vocabulary:** combinations, 5, 5 friends, decompose, compose We have an anchor chart here to help us think about ten friends. The one we made in whole group. **Math Talk:** _____ and _____ make _____. *(Teacher passes out #5 bracelets to every child). Let's look at them. What do you notice?*
Model	**Teacher:** What do you notice about them? **Carla:** They look like the number bracelets. **Teacher:** Today we are going to break apart our number bracelets and then record our work. **Step 1:** Watch what I do. Here is my number bracelet. My number bracelet has 5 beads. I am going to break it into 2 different parts. **Step 2:** I broke it into 3 and 2. 3 and 2 make 5. **Step 3:** Now I am going to record my work on the number bracelet template.
Checking for Understanding	**Teacher:** Does everybody see how to do it? Ok, I am going to give each one of you a number bracelet recording sheet to do your work.

Figure 5.23 Student Activity

Visual Student Activity

Guided Practice/ Checking for Understanding	**Teacher:** Let's do one together. Everybody get your number bracelet ready. Let's break it into 5 and ? *(students answer 0)* Ok, now let's color that on our template. Who can explain what we did? *(student explains)* Ok, now each of you gets to break apart in your own way and then color the template and explain what you did to us. *(Students go around and break apart their number bracelet, record their work and explain it to the group).* *Lilly:* I am going to break it into 4 and 1. **Step 2:** I broke it into 4 and 1. 4 and 1 make 5. **Step 3:** Now I am going to record my work on the number bracelet template. 
Set up for Independent Practice	**Teacher:** What were we working on today? **Vanessa:** We were working on drawing our number bracelets? **Teacher:** Why would we draw our number bracelets? **Teddy:** So we can model! **Teacher:** Yep! We are working on modeling our work. To model our work is to show what we are doing with things or with drawings. We will continue to work on modeling throughout the year because it is one of the things that great mathematicians know how to do! You may all go to your workstations now.

Figure 5.24 Lesson Close

Close
◆ What did we do today?   ◆ What was the math we were practicing?   ◆ Was this easy or tricky?   ◆ Turn to a partner and state one thing you learned today.

Figure 5.25 Recording Sheet

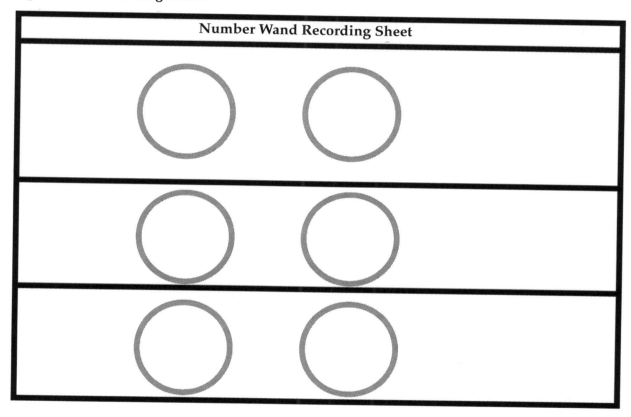

Abstract Lesson

Figure 5.26 Abstract Introduction

	Introduction to Abstract Activity
Launch	**Teacher:** Today we are going to continue to work on making five. Our goal is to learn different "combinations" to five. **Vocabulary:** combinations, 5, five friends, decompose, compose We have an anchor chart here to help us think about five friends. The one we made in whole group. **Math Talk:** _____ and _____ make _____. *(Teacher passes out #5 bracelets to every child). Let's look at them. What do you notice?*
Model	**Teacher:** We are going to play a card game today. Let's look at our make five poster. What does this chart help us to see? **Student:** We can see the different ways to make five. Like 0 and 5. **Teacher:** Who can tell me another way to make five? **Student:** 5 and 0. **Teacher:** Ok, today we are going to see how well you all know your make five friends.
Checking for Understanding	Today we are going to play a card game. It is a match game. We have 20 cards and they are all turned face down. We will take turns trying to find all the matches of ways to make 5. If you get stuck, you can look at our anchor chart. To start, we are going to each roll the dice. Whoever has the largest number starts the game. Then we take turns. The person on your left goes after you and we continue going in that direction. 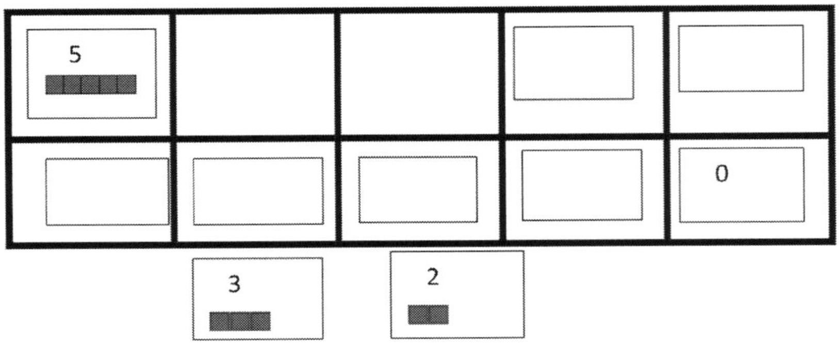

Figure 5.27 Student Activity

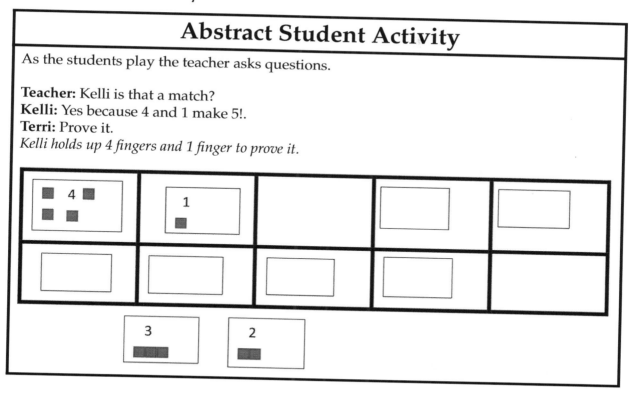

Abstract Student Activity

As the students play the teacher asks questions.

Teacher: Kelli is that a match?
Kelli: Yes because 4 and 1 make 5!.
Terri: Prove it.
Kelli holds up 4 fingers and 1 finger to prove it.

Figure 5.28 Lesson Close

Close

♦ What did we do today?
♦ What was the math we were practicing?
♦ Was this easy or tricky?
♦ Turn to a partner and state one thing you learned today.

Figure 5.29 Cards

1	2	3	4	5
1	2	3	4	5
1	2	3	4	5
0	0			

Figure 5.30 Subtraction Cards

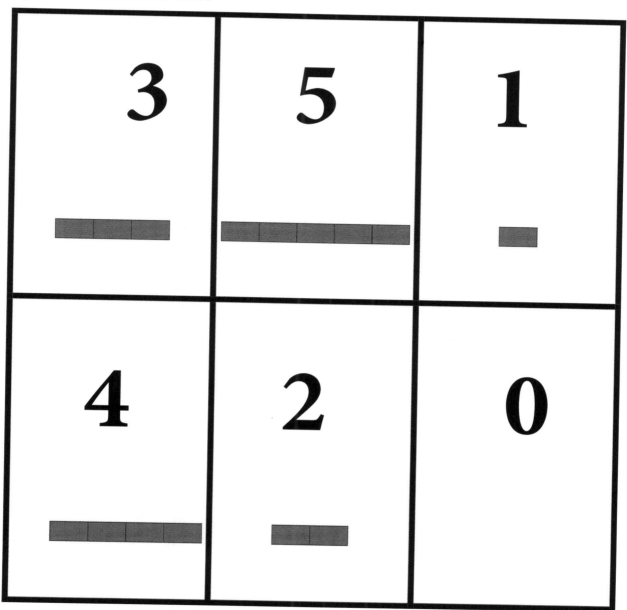

Section Summary

Addition is a very important concept in kindergarten. Students should work through the cycle of engagement, exploring the concept through concrete, pictorial and abstract experiences. In most states, this concept is fluency within 5, although students explore addition within 10 as part of the general standard. Students should be able to add within 5 without any hesitation. Students should understand adding 0 to a number, adding 1 to a number, counting on and making 5.

Subtracting Within 5

Overview

Figure 5.31 Overview

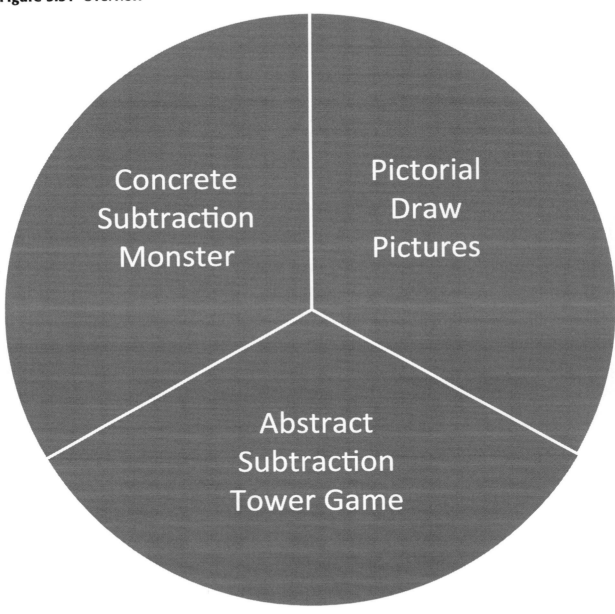

Figure 5.32 Planning Template

Subtraction: Take Away within 5	
Big Idea: Subtraction is about taking away a number from another number.	**Materials**
	♦ Tools: Cubes
Enduring Understanding: We can model subtraction in many ways.	♦ Templates: Monster Template
	♦ Cards
Essential Question: What are the ways to model subtraction?	
I can statement: I can model subtraction in many ways.	
Cycle of Engagement	**Vocabulary & Language Frames**
	♦ Take away
Concrete: Subtraction Machine	♦ Separate
	♦ Subtract
	♦ Difference
5 - 1	♦ Minus Sign
	The difference between ____ and ____ is ____
	____take away ____ is _____
Pictorial: Drawing	
5 – 4 = 1	
Abstract: Match Addends and the Sum	
5 – 4 = 1	
Mathematical Processes/Practices	
♦ **Reasoning**	
♦ **Tools**	
♦ **Modeling**	
♦ **Precision**	

Figure 5.33 Differentiation

Three Differentiated Lessons
In this series of lessons, students are working on the concept of subtraction within 5 using different types of models. They are developing this concept through concrete activities, pictorial activities and abstract activities. Here are some things to think about as you do these lessons.

Emergent	On Grade Level	Above Grade Level
Review counting.	Use different models to represent expressions and equations.	Expand the number range.

 Looking for Misunderstandings and Common Errors

When students are learning to subtract, they have some difficulty. They often will miscount when subtracting and actually count the minuend and lose tract. For example, they will get 5 – 3 as 3 because they will count back 5,4,3 instead of 4,3,2. So have them act it out in real life-size five frames. Also, use number paths where they can actually walk on them and "feel" the count.

Figure 5.34 Anchor Chart

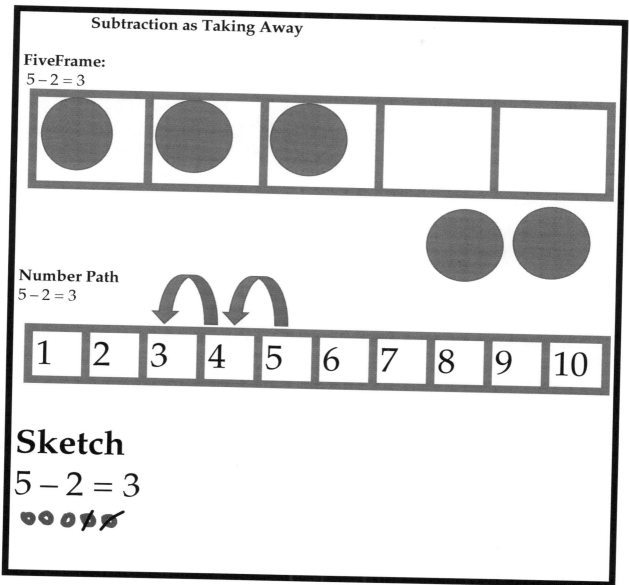

Concrete Lesson

Figure 5.35 Concrete Introduction

Introduction to Concrete Activity
I CAN subtract USING DIFFERENT MODELS.

Launch	**Teacher:** Today we are going to work on subtracting with different models. Let's look at them. What do you notice? Vocabulary: Subtract, take away, separate, minus, difference, big number, small number **There were _____.** **The monster ate _____.** **There are _____ left.**
Model	
Checking for Understanding	**Teacher:** Here we have a hungry monster. He had 4 cookies and he ate 3. How many are left? **Jamil:** 1. **Teacher:** Are you sure? **Katie:** Yes, see it is there at the bottom. **Teacher:** Let's try another one. Let's say he had 4 cookies and he ate 2. Who wants to act that out? **Hong:** I do. See 4 take away 2 is 2. **Teacher:** Who agrees? He took away 2. He put them in the monster's mouth. There are 2 cookies left on the table. **Teacher:** Now you all are each going to have your own Monster Mat.

Figure 5.36 Student Activity

Concrete Student Activity

Guided Practice/ Checking for Understanding	The teacher passes out subtraction cards and Monster Mats. Students pull a card and act out their problems. The students each get a chance to share their problem and explain how they solved it. **Maria:** I had 4 take away 2. I got 2 left. There were _____. The monster ate _____. There are _____ left.
Set up for Independent Practice	**Teacher:** If we wanted to double check the answer what could we do? **Todd:** We could count on our fingers. **Teacher:** Yes, let's do that. You know what. We are going to be talking more about that in the upcoming days. Are there any questions? What was interesting today? What was tricky? **Kayla:** The monster is funny!

Figure 5.37 Lesson Close

Close
◆ What did we do today?
◆ What was the math we were practicing?
◆ Was this easy or tricky?
◆ Turn to a partner and state one thing you learned today.

Figure 5.38 Cards

2 – 1	5 – 0
3 – 2	3 – 0
5 – 5	1 – 1
4 – 3	3 – 3
4 – 2	3 – 1

Figure 5.39 Card

Monster

Visual Lesson

Figure 5.40 Visual Introduction

Introduction Visual Explorations

Launch	Teacher: Today we are going to continue to work on subtracting using math sketches. *Students should talk about what they did last time.*
	Vocabulary: Subtract, take away, separate, minus, difference, big number, small number
	Math Talk: I had _____. I took away _____. I have _____ left.
Model	Teacher: Today we are going to record our thinking with sketches.
	Step 1: Watch what I do. Here is my problem: 5 – 4 = 1
Checking for Understanding	Teacher: Now, what do you notice? Lucy: You drew 5 and crossed out 4. Teacher: How do we know it is correct? Lucy: We can double check. Teacher: We need to count to make sure. Let's check it. It's always good to double check. Tom: 1 is left. Teacher: Interesting…so there are the same. What is another way to think about this? The crossing out is the model. Lucy: You could check. On your fingers too. Teacher: Let's try that. Teacher: Yes. Did you notice how I drew a picture to model my thinking. We can do it by drawing. Ok, now you all are going to try it. I am going to pass around a problem to each person and you will model it and then share your thinking.

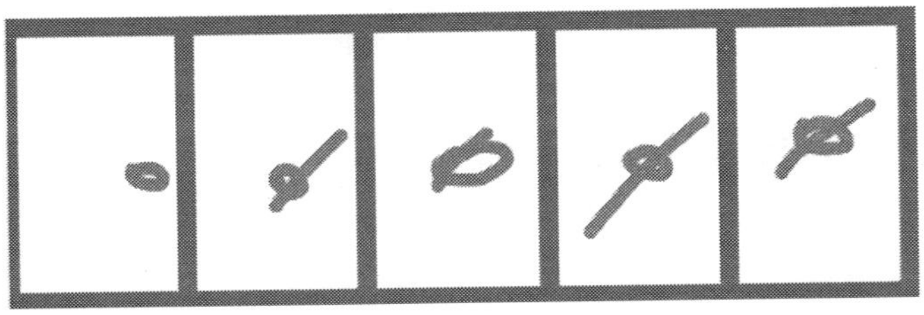

Figure 5.41 Student Activity

<div align="center">**Visual Student Activity**</div>	
Introduction	
Guided Practice/ Checking for Understanding	**Kate:** I used the number path. I started on 5 and I hopped back 2. I got 3. 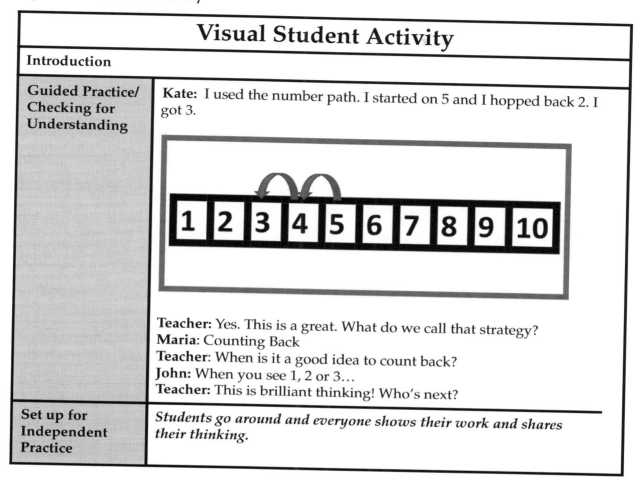 **Teacher:** Yes. This is a great. What do we call that strategy? **Maria:** Counting Back **Teacher:** When is it a good idea to count back? **John:** When you see 1, 2 or 3… **Teacher:** This is brilliant thinking! Who's next?
Set up for Independent Practice	*Students go around and everyone shows their work and shares their thinking.*

Figure 5.42 Lesson Close

<div align="center">**Close**</div>
◆ What did we do today? ◆ What was the math we were practicing? ◆ Was this easy or tricky? ◆ Turn to a partner and state one thing you learned today.

Abstract Lesson

Figure 5.43 Abstract Introduction

	Introduction to the Abstract Lesson I
Launch	**Teacher:** Today we are going to continue to work on subtracting with models. Let's review our vocabulary and our anchor chart. **Vocabulary: subtract, take away, minus, difference** **Math Talk:** ____ take away ____ is ____. Who wants to talk about our vocabulary? **Sara:** Difference is the answer **David:** Subtract means to take away. **Mike:** We use the minus sign in the number sentence to subtract.
Model	**Teacher:** Today we are going to play a game called Race to the tower. You play with a partner. You play rock, paper, scissors to see who starts. Then, you pick a card and move that many spaces. If it says, *Go back 1 or 2,* then you have to move back. If it says *Go ahead 2* then you can move 2 spaces. Here are the cards and here is the game mat. If you need to, you can use tools.

0 – 0	0 – 0
1 – 1	1 – 1
2 – 0	2 – 0
3 – 1	2 – 0
5 – 4	5 – 4
4 – 2	4 – 2
3 – 2	3 – 2
2 – 1	2 – 1
1 – 0	1 – 0

(Continued)

Figure 5.43 (Continued)

	Move 1	Move 2	Move 1
	Move 1	Move 2	Move 1
Checking for Understanding	**Teacher:** Who can explain the game? **Teddy:** You have to pick a card and move. Then you have to say the answer.		

Figure 5.44 Game Cards

Move 1	Move 2	Move 1
Move 1	Move 2	Move 1
Go back 1	Go back 2	Move 1
Go back 1	Go back 2	Move 1
Move 1	Move 2	Move 1
Move 1	Move 2	Move 1
Move 1	Move 2	Move 1

Figure 5.45 Student Activity

	Abstract Student Activity
Introduction	
Guided Practice/ Checking for Understanding	**Kate:** I used the number path. I started on 5 and I hopped back 2. I got 3.
	## I can model subtraction many ways.
	Jonie: I landed on 5 – 4. I did it on my fingers. I put 5 and then took away 5. I have 1 left.
	Mark: My card said go back 2. I landed on 4 -2. That's easy. It's 2. See 4 -2 is 2 (he shows it on his fingers).
	0 - 0 0 - 0
	1 - 1 1 - 1
	2 - 0 2 - 0
	3 - 1 3 - 1
	5 - 4 5 - 4
	4 - 2 4 - 2
	3 - 2 3 - 2
	2 - 1 2 - 1
	1 - 0 1 - 0
	1 2 3 4 5 6 7 8 9 10
	Model Bank: **Drawing, Five frame, number path, counters**
Set up for Independent Practice	**Teacher:** Yes. This is a great. What else could we do to show our thinking?
	Maria: Counting Back
	Teacher: When is it a good idea to **count back?**
	John: When you see 1, 2 or 3…
	Teacher: This is brilliant thinking! Who's next?
	Students go around and everyone shows their work and shares their thinking.

Figure 5.46 Lesson Close

Close
◆ What did we do today?
◆ What was the math we were practicing?
◆ Was this easy or tricky?
◆ Turn to a partner and state one thing you learned today.

Section Summary

Subtraction is a very important concept in kindergarten. Students should work through the cycle of engagement, exploring the concept through concrete, pictorial and abstract experiences. Make sure that students understand the concepts of subtracting 0 from a number, 1 from a number, counting back and taking a number from itself within 5. They should also be exploring subtraction within ten. In most states, this concept is fluency within 5, although students explore subtraction within 10 as part of the general standard. Students should be able to subtract within 5 without any hesitation.

Subtracting with Models

Overview

Figure 5.47 Overview

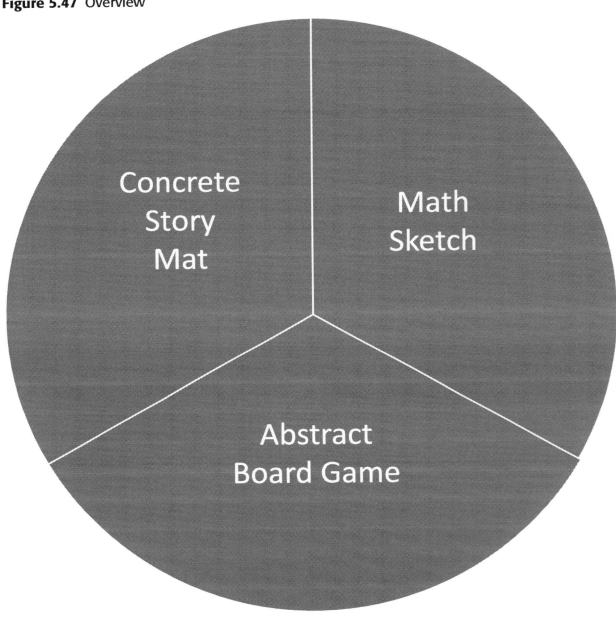

Figure 5.48 Planning Template

Subtraction: Using Math Models

Big Idea: Subtraction is about taking away a number from another number.

Enduring Understanding: We can model subtraction in many ways.

Essential Question: What are the ways to model subtraction?

I can statement: I can model subtraction in many ways.

Materials
♦ Tools: Cubes
♦ Templates: Monster Template
♦ Cards

Cycle of Engagement

Concrete: Bears in a Cave

Pictorial: Drawing
5 − 4 = 1

Abstract: Subtraction Board Game

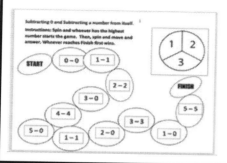

Vocabulary & Language Frames
♦ Take away
♦ Subtract
♦ Difference
♦ Minus Sign
♦ Sum
____ take away ____ is _____
The difference between ____ and ____ is
_____

Levels of Understanding
♦ Emergent
♦ Early Emergent
♦ Fluent
♦ Advanced Fluent

Figure 5.49 Differentiation

Three Differentiated Lessons
In this series of lessons, students are working on the concept of subtracting using different types of models. They are developing this concept through concrete activities, pictorial activities and abstract activities. Here are some things to think about as you do these lessons.

Emerging	On Grade Level	Above Grade Level
Review counting.	Use different models to represent expressions and equations.	Expand the number range.

 Looking for Misunderstandings and Common Errors

Subtraction is tricky for many students. Have them model their thinking with math sketches. Students should understand that a math sketch is quick, not a full drawing. For example, a math sketch is drawing circles for marbles or balls.

Figure 5.50 Anchor Chart

We can subtract with our fingers 	**We can subtract with our five frame.** 
We can subtract with our rekenrek. 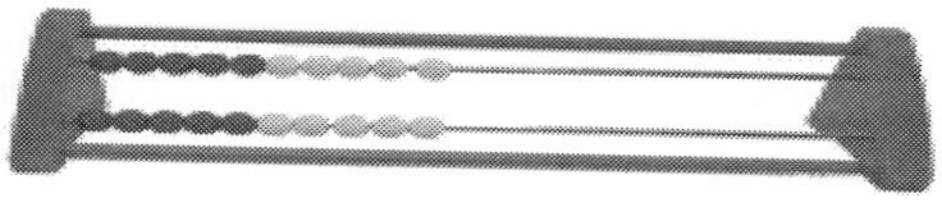	**We can subtract with our drawing.** 
We can subtract on a number path. 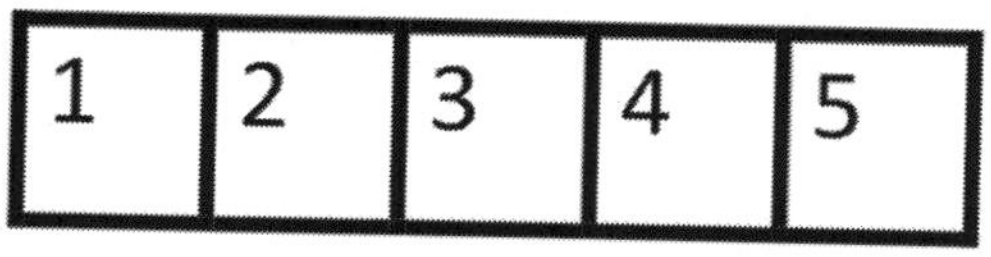 | 1 | 2 | 3 | 4 | 5 |	**We can subtract with counters.** 

Concrete Lesson

Figure 5.51 Concrete Introduction

	Introduction **Concrete Explorations**
Launch	**Teacher:** Today we are going to work on subtracting with different models. Let's look at them. What do you notice? **Vocabulary: Subtract, take away, minus, difference, big number, small number** **Math Talk: I had _____. I took away _____. I have _____ left.**
Model	**Teacher:** Ok, we are going to tell subtraction stories. I am going to show you a subtraction mat and you are going to tell us the story. Who wants to go first to act out this story ? **Stephanie:** I do. There are 3 bears. 1 goes inside the cave. How many bears are left outside? **Marta:** 2 **Teacher:** Great story! Does everybody agree? How do you know she is correct? How could we check? **Marcus:** Well if we put the 2 here inside and we have 1 on the outside. There was 3 and 1 went in the cave. On my fingers I have 3 and take away 1 is 2.
Checking for Understanding	The students continue telling stories.

Figure 5.52 Student Activity

Concrete Student Activity

Guided Practice/ Checking for Understanding	**Teacher:** Ok, today we are going to tell subtraction stories. I am going to show you a subtraction mat and you are going to tell us the story. Who wants to go first to act out this story?  There are 5 bears. 3 went in the cave. How many are outside? _____ + _____ = _____ **James:** I do. **James:** I put 3 in the cave and 2 on the outside. **Teacher:** Great story! Does everybody agree? How do you know she is correct? How could we check? **Kayla:** Well if we put the 3 here inside and we have 2 on the outside. There was 5 and 3 went in the cave. On my fingers I have 5 and take away 3 and that leaves 2.
Set up for Independent Practice	The students continue telling stories. Afterwards the teacher asks the students about the math they did today. Then, students go to their workstations.

Figure 5.53 Lesson Close

Close
◆ What did we do today?
◆ What was the math we were practicing?
◆ Was this easy or tricky?
◆ Turn to a partner and state one thing you learned today.

Figure 5.54 Word Problem Cards (Editor Note: ALL 1 figure)

There are 4 . 2 went in the cave . How many are outside?

There are 5 bears . 3 went in the cave . How many are outside?

There are 3 bears . 1 went in the cave . How many are outside?

There are 4 bears . 3 went in the cave . How many are outside?

There are 3 bears . 2 went in the cave . How many are outside?

Figure 5.55 Bear Cards

Visual Lesson

Figure 5.56 Visual Introduction

<table>
<tr>
<td colspan="2" align="center"><h2>Introduction
Visual Explorations</h2></td>
</tr>
<tr>
<td>Launch</td>
<td>

Teacher: Today we are going to work on subtracting with different models. Let's look at them. What do you notice?

Vocabulary: Subtract, take away, minus, difference, big number, small number

Math Talk: I had _____. I took away _____. I have _____ left.

</td>
</tr>
<tr>
<td>Model</td>
<td>

Teacher: Ok, we are going to tell subtraction stories. I am going to show you a subtraction mat and you are going to tell us a story. Your story should fit in the 5 frame just for right now. We are practicing what happens when you take away all. Tell us how you might use the different models.

Tori: I can do this. There were 2 bears. They both left. How many are there now? I drew it in the 5 frame and I hopped on the number path.

</td>
</tr>
<tr>
<td>Checking for Understanding</td>
<td>

Teacher: What do you all think?
Mary: I think she did a great job. I like the way she modeled it on the 5 frame.
Teacher: I am going to give you all the mat to tell a story and then draw it out.

</td>
</tr>
</table>

Figure 5.57 Student Activity

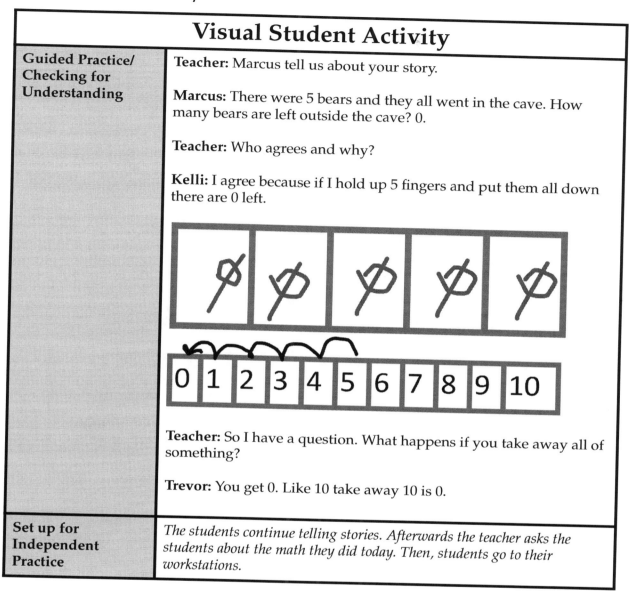

Guided Practice/ Checking for Understanding	**Teacher:** Marcus tell us about your story. **Marcus:** There were 5 bears and they all went in the cave. How many bears are left outside the cave? 0. **Teacher:** Who agrees and why? **Kelli:** I agree because if I hold up 5 fingers and put them all down there are 0 left. **Teacher:** So I have a question. What happens if you take away all of something? **Trevor:** You get 0. Like 10 take away 10 is 0.
Set up for Independent Practice	*The students continue telling stories. Afterwards the teacher asks the students about the math they did today. Then, students go to their workstations.*

Figure 5.58 Lesson Close

Close

◆ What did we do today?
◆ What was the math we were practicing?
◆ Was this easy or tricky?
◆ Turn to a partner and state one thing you learned today.

Abstract Lesson

Figure 5.59 Abstract Introduction

	Introduction Abstract Explorations
Launch	**Teacher:** Today we are going to work on subtracting. We are going to play a board game. If you need to use some of the models we have been working with you can. **Vocabulary: Subtract, take away, minus, difference, big number, small number** **Math Talk: I had _____. I took away _____. I have _____ left.**
Model	**Teacher:** To play we will spin. Whoever has the largest number starts the game. Spin and move and answer. Whoever reaches Finish first wins. 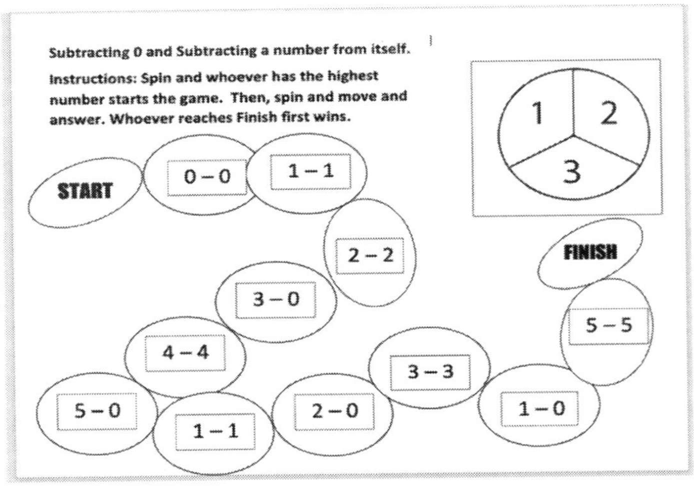
Checking for Understanding	**Teacher:** Does everybody understand how to play. It is a board game like we always play. **Ricardo:** You spin and then you move and answer the question. You have to reach finish to win.

Figure 5.60 Student Activity

	Student Abstract Activity
Guided Practice/ Checking for Understanding	*As the students play the game, the teacher asks questions.* **Teacher:** Trevor tell me how you solved the problem you landed on. **Trevor:** I landed on 3 – 0. That is 3. **Teacher:** Who has a question? **Marta:** How do you know? **Trevor:** Because 3 minus 0 is 3. (He shows this on his fingers). **Teacher:** Ok, I think we are ready to play with partners. Remember it's only a game and we are just practicing our math. If you win, you win with dignity. If you lose, you also lose with dignity. 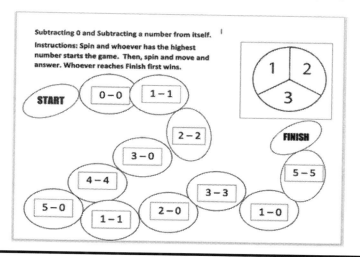
Set up for Independent Practice	**Teacher:** Ok, today what did we work on today? **Trevor:** We worked on subtraction. **Marta:** We were subtracting all. **Lucy:** We were also subtracting 0. **Teacher:** What does all that mean? **Timmy:** When you take away 0 you are taking away nothing. So the answer is the number. **Kelli:** And when you take away all you get 0. **Teacher:** Wow! I like the thinking. I celebrate the explaining. You are all such great mathematicians. I also really like how I saw you using models when you got stuck. We are going to put this game in the workstations so you all can practice. Are there any questions? Ok, you can go to your workstations now.

Figure 5.61 Lesson Close

Close
◆ What did we do today?
◆ What was the math we were practicing?
◆ Was this easy or tricky?
◆ Turn to a partner and state one thing you learned today.

Section Summary

Teaching subtraction is foundational. Students need to actually do many subtraction problems on different models, including the ten frame, rekenrek and number lines. There should be an equal amount of time spent on subtraction as on addition, and the connections between the two should be constantly being made. The research says that subtraction is much more difficult for children than addition (Kamii, Kirkland, & Lewis, 2001, p. 33). It is important for students to master addition so that they can use that knowledge to help them with subtraction (Kamii, Kirkland, & Lewis, 2001). Make sure to build a strong foundation with concrete materials and drawings before rushing students to solve just abstract problems.

Depth of Knowledge

Depth of Knowledge is a framework that encourages us to ask questions that require that students think, reason, explain, defend and justify their thinking (Webb, 2002). Here is a snapshot of what that can look like in terms of fluency work. It is important to continually reflect on what the level of the lesson is. In working in small groups on problem solving, be sure to ask open questions so that students can think and reason out loud with others.

Figure 5.62 DOK Chart

	What are different strategies and models that we can use to explore addition word problems?	What are different strategies and models to explore combinations within 5?	What are different strategies and models that we can use to explore subtraction facts within 5?	What are different strategies and models that we can use to explore subtraction word problems?
DOK Level 1 (These are questions where students are required to simply recall/reproduce an answer/do a procedure.)	Solve: There are 2 monkeys and 1 zebra. How many animals are there?	Solve: 4 + 0	Solve: 3 – 1	Solve: There were 5 candies. The monster ate 2. How many are left?
DOK Level 2 (These are questions where students have to use information, think about concepts and reason.) This is considered a more challenging problem than a level 1 problem.	There are 2 monkeys and 2 zebras. Model and solve this problem in 2 different ways.	If I say 2, how many more to 5? If I say 4, how many more to 5?	Tell me 2 ways to prove that 5 – 2 = 3.	There were 5 candies. The monster ate 2. How many are left? Model and solve this problem in 2 different ways.
DOK Level 3 (These are questions where students have to reason, plan, explain, justify and defend their thinking.)	Tell me an addition story. Model and solve it. Explain how you know your answer is correct.	Give me an example of a make 5 fact. Model it in two different ways. Explain how you know your answer is correct.	Give me an example of a subtraction problem. Model it and solve it.	Tell me a subtraction story. Model and solve it. Explain how you know your answer is correct.

Figure 5.63 Asking Rigorous Questions

DOK 1	DOK 2 — At this level students explain their thinking.	DOK 3 — At this level students have to justify, defend and prove their thinking with objects, drawings and diagrams.
What is the answer to ??? Can you model the problem? Can you identify the answer that matches this equation?	How do you know that the equation is correct? Can you pick the correct answer and explain why it is correct? How can you model that problem in more than one way? What is another way to model that problem? Can you model that on the . . . ??? Give me an example of a . . . type of problem. Which answer is incorrect? Explain your thinking.	Can you prove that your answer is correct? Prove that . . . Explain why that is the answer. Show me how to solve that and explain what you are doing.

Resources

A great resource for asking open questions is Marion Small's *Good Questions: Great ways to differentiate mathematics instruction in the standards-based classroom* (2017). Also, Robert Kaplinsky has done a great job in pushing our thinking forward with the Depth of Knowledge Matrices he created (https://robertkaplinsky.com/depth-knowledge-matrix-elementary-math/). Kentucky Math Department (2007) has these great math matrices as well.

Key Points

- Addition within 5 facts
- Addition within 10 facts
- Subtraction within 5 facts
- Subtraction within 10 facts

Chapter Summary

It is essential that we work on basic fact fluency with students in small guided math groups. We have to take them through the cycle of concrete, pictorial and abstract activities. We need to make sure that students understand, can explain and appropriately use the various strategies. Just because the textbook is teaching a specific strategy, in no way implies that the students are actually ready to be working on that strategy. Therefore, it is essential that we pull groups and work with students in their zone of proximal development. We then follow this work up with workstations and homework that correlates with the concepts they are working on. Fluency is a continuum and all the students are working toward the grade level fluency, but they are not all starting at the same point at the same time.

Reflection Questions

1. How are you currently teaching basic math fact fluency?
2. Are you making sure that you do concrete, pictorial and abstract activities?
3. What do your students struggle with the most, and what ideas are you taking away from this chapter that might inform your work around those struggles?

References

Baroody, J., Purpura, D., Eiland, M., Reid, E., & Paliwal, V. (2016). Does Fostering Reasoning Strategies for Relatively Difficult Combinations Promote Transfer by k-3 Students? *Journal of Educational Psychology*, 108(4).

Bay-Williams, J., & Kling, B. (2019). *Math Fact Fluency*. Reston, VA: ASCD.

Boaler, J. (2015). *Fluency Without Fear: Research Evidence on the Best Ways to Learn Math Facts*. Retrieved September 6, 2019 from www.youcubed.org/evidence/fluency-without-fear/

Brownell, W. A. (1956, October/1987). Meaning and Skill—Maintaining the Balance. *Arithmetic Teacher*, 3, 129–136.

Brownell, W. A., & Chazal, C. B. (1935, September). The Effects of Premature Drill in Third-Grade Arithmetic. *Journal of Educational Research*, 29, 17–28.

Godfrey, C., & Stone, J. (2013). Mastering Fact Fluency: Are They Game? *Teaching Children Mathematics*, 20(2), 96–101.

Henry, V., & Brown, R. (2008). First-Grade Basic Facts: An Investigation into Teaching and Learning of an Accelerated, High-Demand Memorization Standard. *Journal for Research in Mathematics Education*, 39(2), 153–183.

Kamii, C., Kirkland, L., & Lewis, B. (2001). Fluency in Subtraction Compared with Addition. *Journal of Mathematical Behavior*, 20, 33–42.

Kentucky Department of Education. (2007). *Support Materials for Core Content for Assessment Version 4.1 Mathematics*. Retrieved January 15, 2017 from the internet.

Kilpatrick, J., Swafford, J., & Findell, B. (Eds.). (2001). *Adding It Up: Helping Children Learn Mathematics*. Mathematics Learning Study Committee, Center for Education, Division of Behavioral and Social Sciences and Education, National Research Council. Washington, DC: National Academy Press.

National Center for Education Evaluation and Regional Assistance. (2009). *Assisting Students Struggling with Mathematics: Response to Intervention (RtI) for Elementary and Middle Schools. 2009–4060*. Retrieved IES from http://ies.ed.gov/ncee and http://ies.ed.gov/ncee/wwc/publications/practiceguides/

Newton, R., Record, A., & Mello, A. (2020). *Fluency Doesn't Just Happen: Teaching Addition and Subtraction*. New York: Routledge.

Small, M. (2017). *Good Questions: Great Ways to Differentiate Math in the Standards Based Classroom*. New York: Teachers College Press.

Thornton, C. (1978). Emphasizing Thinking Strategies in Basic Fact Instruction. *Journal for Research in Mathematics Education*, 9(3), 214–225. Reston, VA: NCTM.

Van de Walle, J. A. (2007). *Elementary and Middle School Mathematics: Teaching Developmentally*. Boston, MA: Pearson/Allyn and Bacon.

Webb, N. (2002). An Analysis of the Alignment Between Mathematics Standards and Assessments for Three States. Paper presented at the *Annual Meeting of the American Educational Research Association*. New Orleans, LA.

6

Small Group Word Problem Lessons

Word problems are an essential part of kindergarten. Students are exposed to several types of problems, strategies and models. We want students to build a foundation for word problems. Problem solving should be done every day. We should work with the whole class, in small groups sometimes and have a workstation that stays up all year long. The important part about teaching word problems is to get students to understand what is happening in the word problem. So they need to think about it, discuss it, explain it and then work it out in a couple of ways. Remember that we must go beyond answer getting. It is about reasoning, communicating and modeling the situations. We want students to be able to solve one way and check another. We want students to be able to look at the answer and decide whether or not it makes sense. We need students to know how to persevere and keep on working with the problem when they get stuck.

Research Note

- ♦ Students have a tendency to "suspend sense-making" when they are solving problems. They don't stop to reason through the problem Schoenfeld, 1991; Verschaffel, Greer, & De Corte). We must find ways to slow the process down so they can think.
- ♦ Students develop a "compulsion to calculate" (Stacey & MacGregor, 1999) that can interfere with the development of the algebraic thinking that is needed to solve word problems (cited in www.cde.state.co.us/comath/word-problems-guide).
- ♦ Research consistently states that we should never use key words. From the beginning, teach students to reason about the context, not to depend on key words. See a great blog post that cites many articles on this: https://gfletchy.com/2015/01/12/teaching-key-words-forget-about-it/

In this chapter, we will look at how to take a deep dive into these discussions with students in small groups. We will look at:

- ♦ Add to result unknown problems
- ♦ Part-part whole problems
- ♦ Take from result unknown problems
- ♦ Part-part whole both addends unknown
- ♦ 3 read problems
- ♦ Picture prompt word problems

DOI: 10.4324/9781003169529-6

Add to Result Unknown Word Problems

Overview

Figure 6.1 Overview

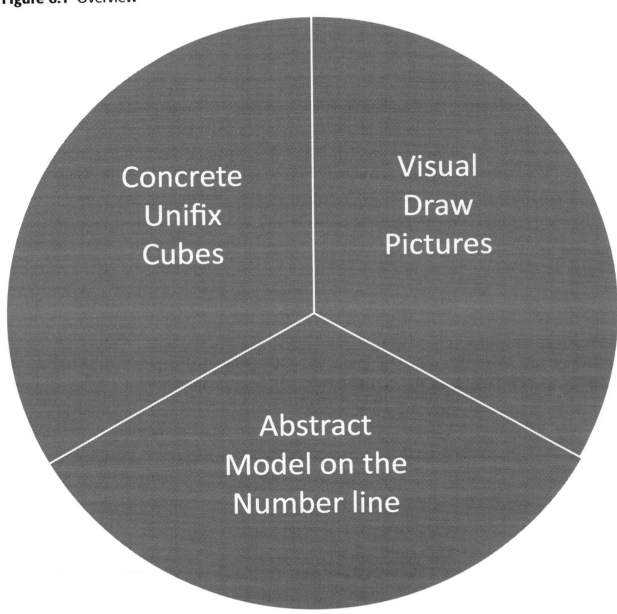

Figure 6.2 Planning Template

Add to Result Unknown Word Problems

Big Idea: There are different types of word problems. In this type, we know the start and the change. We are looking for what happened at the end.

Enduring Understanding: We can model problems in many ways.

Essential Question: What are the ways to model this type of problem?

I can statement: I can model addition word problems.

Materials
- Tools: Cubes
- Templates: Ten Frame
- Cards
- Crayons

**Cycle of Engagement
Concrete:**

Visual: Drawing

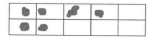

Abstract: Match Addends and the Sum

Sue had 4 marbles. She got 2 more. How many does she have now?	Pick a model. Solve. Number Path Grid Paper Drawing Ten Frame Rekenrek

Vocabulary & Language Frames

- Addend
- Add
- Plus
- Sum

_____ started with _____.
_____ got ____more.
Now there are _____.

**Questions
What is happening in this problem?**

Math Processes/Practices
- **Reasoning**
- **Modeling**
- **Tools**
- **Precision**

Figure 6.3 Differentiation

| **Three Differentiated Lessons** |
| In this series of lessons, students are working on the concept of *add to problems*. They are developing this concept through concrete activities, visual activities and abstract activities. Everybody should do the cycle. Some students progress through it more quickly than others. Here are some things to think about as you do these lessons. |

Emergent	On Grade Level	Above Grade Level
Review adding. As you introduce this to students, do a lot of work by acting it out and then doing it with manipulatives. Be sure to have students draw what they acted out and connect it to number models.	The grade level standard is that students can model it and explain it. So do lots of this work where students are modeling it and explaining it. Also show and talk about exemplars and non-exemplars of this concept.	Move to doing more abstract activities with formal word problems.

 ## Looking for Misunderstandings and Common Errors

These are the easiest types of word problems for students to solve. Sometimes they make counting and adding errors. So, it is really important to use tools and have students double check and explain how they found the answer. I always like to ask them, "Are you sure about that?" I especially ask them that when they have the correct answer, because I want them to be able to defend their thinking.

Figure 6.4 Anchor Chart

Solving Add to Result Unknown Problems

Jane has 2 rings. She got 1 more. How many does she have now?

Ten Frame:
2 + 1 = ?

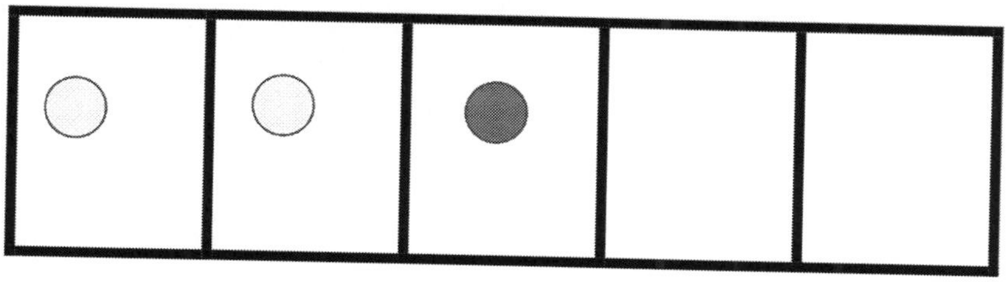

Number Path

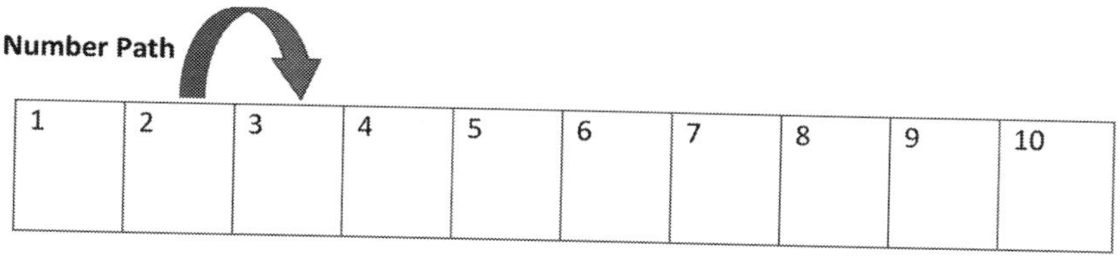

1	2	3	4	5	6	7	8	9	10

Sketch

Concrete Lesson

Figure 6.5 Concrete Introduction

Introduction
Explore Concrete Activities

Launch	**Teacher:** Today we are going to work on solving word problems. **Vocabulary: add, change, word problem, sum** **Math Talk: I had _____. I got ____more. Now I have _____ . How many do I have now?** **Listen to the problem.** I had 4 jewels. I got 4 more. How many do I have now? Now, who has some ideas how I could model that problem? **Jack:** You can count up. 4, 5,6,7, 8 **Teacher:** Excellent! That is a strategy. Now, tell me how you could model that strategy? **Lucy:** We could use the counters. **Teacher:** Show me. **Lucy:** Here are 4 cubes and then 4 more makes 8.

Model	**Teacher:** This is great! So we can model it with cubes. What is another way to model that problem? **David:** The rekenrek ….see I had 4 and I moved 4 more over to get 8 (he uses the digital version from Math Learning Center one on an Ipad).
Checking for Understanding	**Teacher:** Ok. Let's do another one. Be ready to talk about different ways to do it. I am going to watch you and if you need help, look at our anchor charts, ask your partners and of course you can ask me.

Figure 6.6 Student Activity

	Concrete Student Activity
Guided Practice/ Checking for Understanding	The teacher passes out the problems. Students pull a card and act out their problems with whatever tool they choose. The students each get a chance to share their problem and explain how they solved it. **Maria: My problem is this:** I had 3 🍎 apples. I got 1 more 🍎 apple. How many do I have now? So, I used my rekenrek and I moved over 3. Then, I moved 1 more and I have 4. 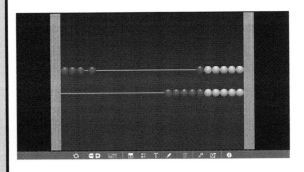 **Teacher:** Why did you move 3 over? **Maria:** Because it said I had 3. **Teacher:** Who agrees with her? **Hong:** I do. I moved over 3 and then 1 more. That's 4. **Teacher:** That is great! You know it automatically. I also need you to show me how you might model it.

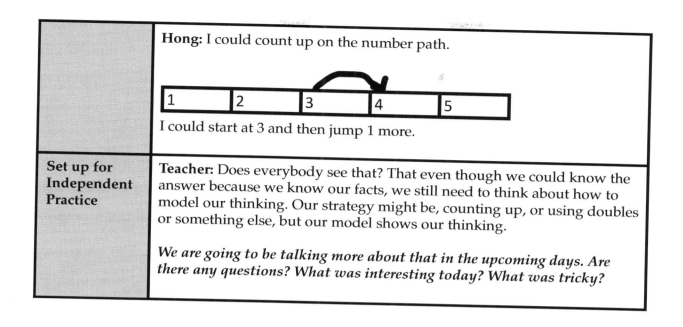

	Hong: I could count up on the number path. | 1	2	3	4	5 | I could start at 3 and then jump 1 more.
Set up for Independent Practice	**Teacher:** Does everybody see that? That even though we could know the answer because we know our facts, we still need to think about how to model our thinking. Our strategy might be, counting up, or using doubles or something else, but our model shows our thinking. *We are going to be talking more about that in the upcoming days. Are there any questions? What was interesting today? What was tricky?*

Figure 6.7 Lesson Close

Close
◆ What did we do today? ◆ What was the math we were practicing? ◆ Was this easy or tricky? ◆ Turn to a partner and state one thing you learned today.

Visual Lesson

Figure 6.8 Visual Introduction

Introduction
Explore Visual Activities

Launch	**Teacher:** Today we are going to work on solving word problems with pictures. **Vocabulary: add, change, word problem, count up,** **Math Talk: There was_____. _____more came. How many are there now?** **Teacher:** Listen to the problem. My problem is this: There was **1** 🐘. **2** more  🐘🐘 came. How many animals are there now?
Model	**Teacher:** Think about our toolkit. What could we use to model this problem? **Taylor:** I know the answer is 3. Because 1 plus 2 is 3. **Teacher:** Great! How do you know? Remember good mathematicians can model their thinking! **Virginia:** Like we do on the whiteboard. I could draw 1 circle and then 2 more. **Teacher:** Great modeling.
Checking for Understanding	**Teacher:** Does anybody agree? Students say yes. **Teacher:** Ok. I am going to give each one of you your own problem. I want you to read it. Solve it. Be ready to share how you did it. I am going to watch you and if you need help, look at our anchor charts , ask a math partner and of course you can ask me.

Figure 6.9 Student Activity

Visual Student Activity

Guided Practice/ Checking for Understanding	The teacher passes out word problem cards. Students pull a card and model their problems. The students each get a chance to share their problem and explain how they solved it. **Maria:** My problem is this: *There were 3 [animals] and 2 [animals] **more came**. How many animals are there now?* **Maria:** There are 3 giraffes and 2 more came. That makes 5 animals. **Teacher:** How do you know you are correct? **Maria:** Because I counted up 2 more. **Teacher:** Who agrees with her? And can you prove it? **Grace:** I do. I counted on my fingers. **David:** 2 and 3 make 5.
Set up for Independent Practice	**Teacher:** That is great! You know it automatically. I am also glad that we can model it. **Teacher:** Does everybody see that? That even though we could know the answer because we know our facts, we still need to think about how to model our thinking. Our strategy might be, counting up, or using doubles or something else, but our model shows our thinking. *Teacher gives everybody a chance to do and discuss a problem. After everyone has shared the lesson ends.* **We are going to be talking more about that in the upcoming days. Are there any questions? What was interesting today? What was tricky?**

Figure 6.10 Lesson Close

Close
◆ What did we do today?   ◆ What was the math we were practicing?   ◆ Was this easy or tricky?   ◆ Turn to a partner and state one thing you learned today.

Figure 6.11 Word Problems

There was **1**  and **2**  more came. How many animals are there now?	There were **3**  and **2**  **more** **came**. How many animals are there now?	There were **4**   and **1** **more**  came. How many animals are there now?
There were **2**   and 5 more   came. How many animals are there now?	There were **3**  and **2**  **more came**. How many animals are there now?	There were **4**   and **1 more**  came. How many animals are there now?

Abstract Lesson

Figure 6.12 Abstract Introduction

	Introduction Exploring with abstract activities
Launch	**Teacher:** Today we are going to continue to work on solving word problems. **Vocabulary: add, change, word problem, count up, number sentence (equation)** **Math Talk: There were _____ _____. _____ more came. How many are there now?**
Model	**Teacher:** Today, we are going to look at storytelling cards and look at the equation that matches. Here is our first one. Who wants to tell a word problem about the picture. And then talk about the number match. 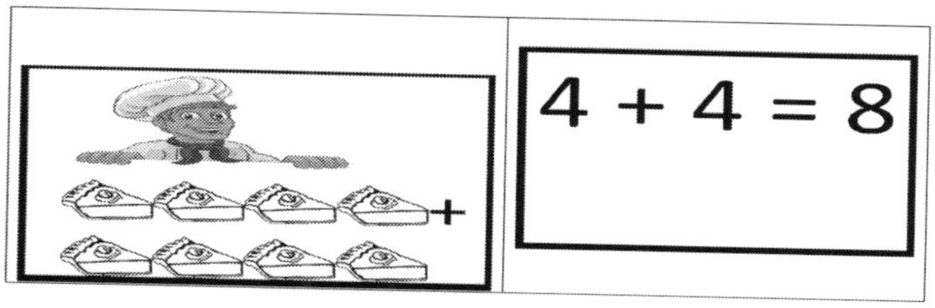 **Ted:** The baker made 4 pieces of pie. Then he made 4 more. Now he has 8.
Checking for Understanding	**Sue:** The kids picked 3 pumpkins and then 2 more. They have 5. 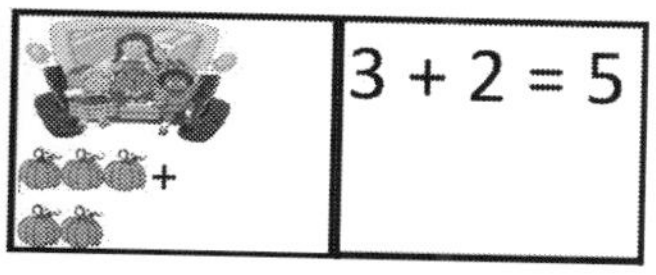 **Sue:** 3 and 2 make 5. Here is the number card to match. **Teacher:** Yes!

Figure 6.13 Student Activity

	Abstract Student Activity
Guided Practice/ Checking for Understanding	The teacher shows the children how to match the picture word problem cards that go together. **Josephine explains:** The kids pick 5 pumpkins and then 3 more. 5 + 3 is 7. I mean 8.  $$5 + 3 = 7$$ **Teacher:** Good catch! Did everybody see how she changed her answer. Good mathematicians are always double checking and thinking about their thinking.
Set up for Independent Practice	*Everybody models the problems.* *Teacher: We are going to be talking more about that in the upcoming days. Are there any questions? What was interesting today? What was tricky?*

Figure 6.14 Lesson Close

Close
◆ What did we do today? ◆ What was the math we were practicing? ◆ Was this easy or tricky? ◆ Turn to a partner and state one thing you learned today.

Figure 6.15 Word Problem Cards

Section Summary

It is important for students to be able to act out these problems in life-size templates such as five frames, ten frames, twenty frames, part-part whole mats, number bonds and number lines. They should also have a mini paper version for their problem solving notebooks. We need students to see how they can model their thinking using different tools. We also need them to recognize the relationship between the number model and the situation.

Part-Part Whole Problems

Overview

Figure 6.16 Overview

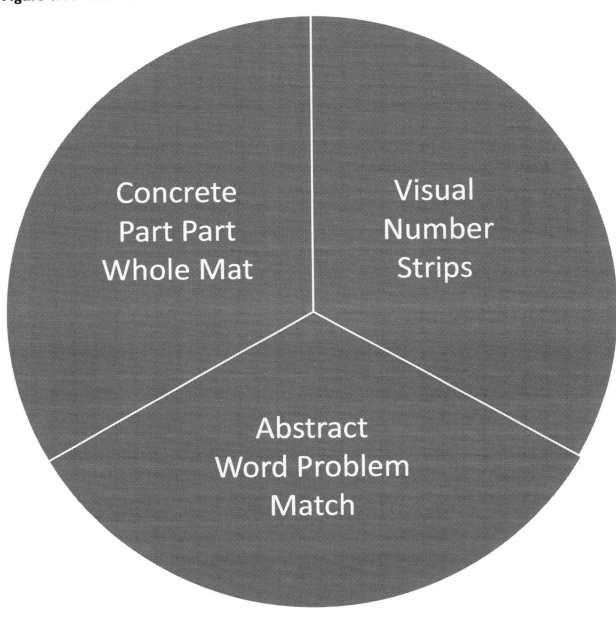

Figure 6.17 Planning Template

Part-Part Whole Problems

Big Idea: There are different types of word problems. In this type, we know know both parts.

Enduring Understanding: We can model problems in many ways.

Essential Question: What are the ways to model this type of problem?

I can statement: I can model part-part whole word problems.

Materials
♦ Tools: Cubes
♦ Templates: Ten Frame
♦ Cards
♦ Crayons

Cycle of Engagement

Concrete:

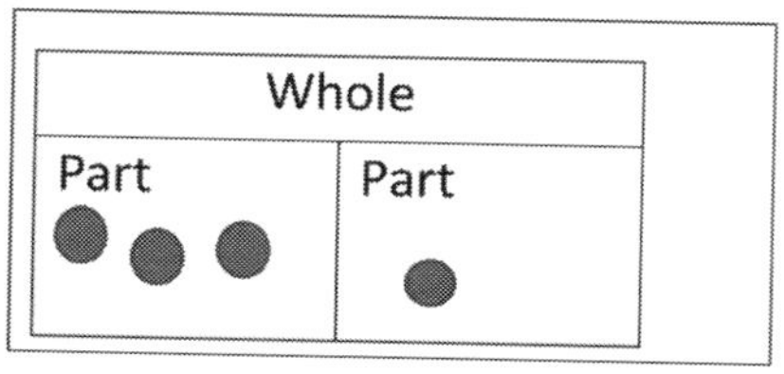

Visual: Drawing

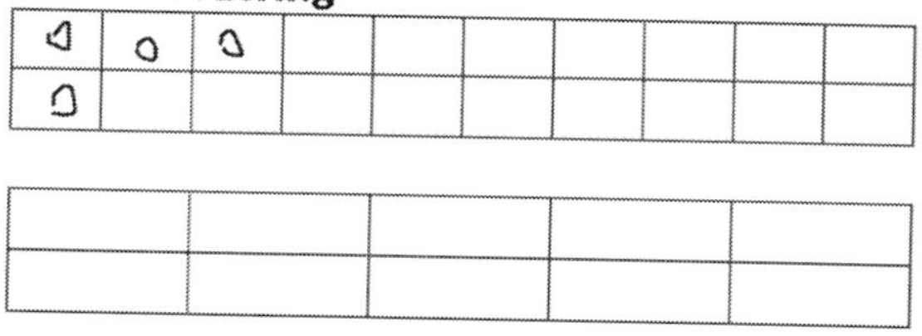

Abstract:: Match Addends and the Sum

| 3 + 1 | 4 |

Vocabulary & Language Frames

♦ Count Up
♦ Addends
♦ Sum
♦ Difference

_____ and _____ make _____.

Figure 6.18 Differentiation

Three Differentiated Lessons

In this series of lessons, students are working on the concept of *part-part whole problems.* They are developing this concept through concrete activities, visual activities and abstract activities. Everybody should do the cycle. Some students progress through it more quickly than others. Here are some things to think about as you do these lessons.

Emergent	On Grade Level	Above Grade Level
Review adding. As you introduce this to students, do a lot of work by acting it out and then doing it with manipulatives. Be sure to have students draw what they acted out and connect it to number models.	The grade level standard is that students can model it and explain it. So do lots of this work where students are modeling it and explaining it. Also show and talk about exemplars and nonexemplars of this concept.	You could extend the number range or the type of problem.

 Looking for Misunderstandings and Common Errors

Part-part whole problems are usually easy for students. Be sure to use part-part whole mats and templates. Also use number bonds. Use these templates with the manipulatives first, before you go to visual and abstract representations.

Figure 6.19 Anchor Chart

Solving Part-Part Whole Problems

Jane has some rings. Five rings are square and the 3 are circles. How many rings does she have?

Ten Frame:
5 + 3 = ?

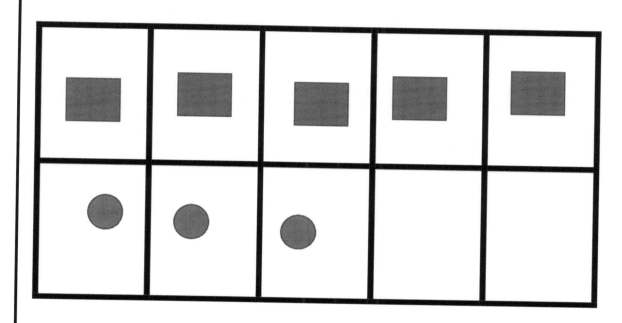

Number Path

1	2	3	4	5	6	7	8	9	10

Sketch

Concrete Lesson

Figure 6.20 Concrete Introduction

	Introduction Exploring with Concrete Explorations
Launch	**Teacher:** Today we are going to work on word problems. We are word problem detectives. We are going to be looking and thinking about the parts we know and don't know! **Vocabulary:** part- part whole, whole, word problem, count up, **Math Talk:** The whole is _____. One part is _____. The other part is _____.
Model	**Teacher:** Listen to the problem. Jamal had some marbles. 5 were big and the 2 were small. How many marbles does he have? **Jack:** 7 **Teacher:** How do you know? **Jack:** I know because 5 and 2 make 7. **Teacher:** Can anyone check that with a model? **Lucy:** I held up 5 and then 2 and now I have 7. **Teacher:** Let's put our information in our Part-Part Whole Mat. In the Part-Part- Whole mat, I am going to put the 5 big marbles in one of the parts, and the two small marbles in the other part. I am wondering what is the whole? **Teacher:** So what do we see? **David:** We see the 5 and we can count 6,7. **Mary:** So we have 7 altogether
Checking for Understanding	*Teacher reads 2 more problems that the group discusses.* *Teacher: Ok. I am going to give each one of you your own problem. I want you to read it. Solve it. Be ready to share how you did it. I am going to watch you and if you need help, look at our anchor charts and of course you can ask me.*

Figure 6.21 Student Activity

Concrete Student Activity

Guided Practice/ Checking for Understanding	The teacher passes out the problems. Students pull a card and act out their problems. The students each get a chance to share their problem and explain how they solved it. **Timmy: My problem is this:** 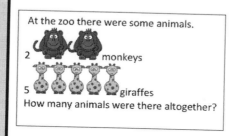 So I used my part-part whole mat and I saw 2 here and 5 here. That makes 7. 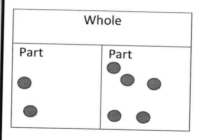 **Teacher:** If I am going to count them how would I do it? **Kayla:** Start with the big number and count on. **David:** Like 5 – 6,7.
Set up for Independent Practice	**Teacher:** Ok. Who wants to go next? *Every child shares out their problem and how they solved it on the Part – Part whole mat. We are going to be talking more about that in the upcoming days. Are there any questions? What was interesting today? What was tricky?*

Figure 6.22 Lesson Close

Close
◆ What did we do today?
◆ What was the math we were practicing?
◆ Was this easy or tricky?
◆ Turn to a partner and state one thing you learned today.

Figure 6.23 Part-Part Whole Cards

There are some animals. 5 🐒 and 2 🦓. How many animals are there?

Whole	
Part	Part

There are some animals. 3 🐒 and 2 🦓. How many animals are there?

Whole	
Part	Part

There are some animals. 2 🐒 and 2 🦓. How many animals?

Whole	
Part	Part

There are some animals. 6 🐒 and 2 🦓. How many animals?

Whole	
Part	Part

Visual Lesson

Figure 6.24 Visual Introduction

	Introduction **Exploring with Visual Explorations**
Launch	**Teacher:** Today we are going to work on solving word problems where we talk about the parts. We are going to act them out on the rekenrek. **Vocabulary:** part-part whole, whole, word problem, count up, number sentence (equation), missing number **Math Talk:** One part is _____. The other part is _____. The whole is _____.
Model	**Teacher:** There were 5 brown bunnies and 3 gray bunnies. How many bunnies are there? So, first act it out on your Rekenrek. Then we are going to draw it on our Rekenrek paper. So first, let's all model it on our Rekenreks. Ok let's see. Now, let's draw it on the paper. Ok. Now what number shall we circle. 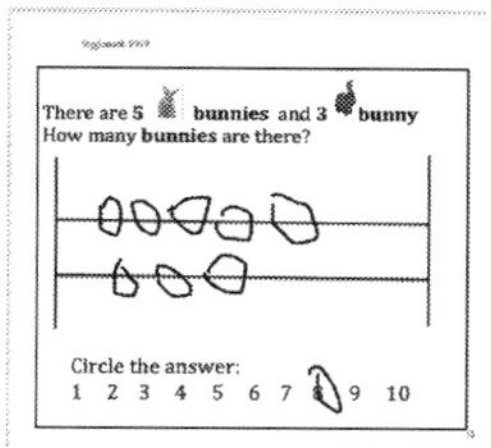 **Marcus:** 8 because 5 and 3 make 8. Here it is. I drew it. I circled 8.
Checking for Understanding	*Students continue to do a few more together.*

Figure 6.25 Student Activity

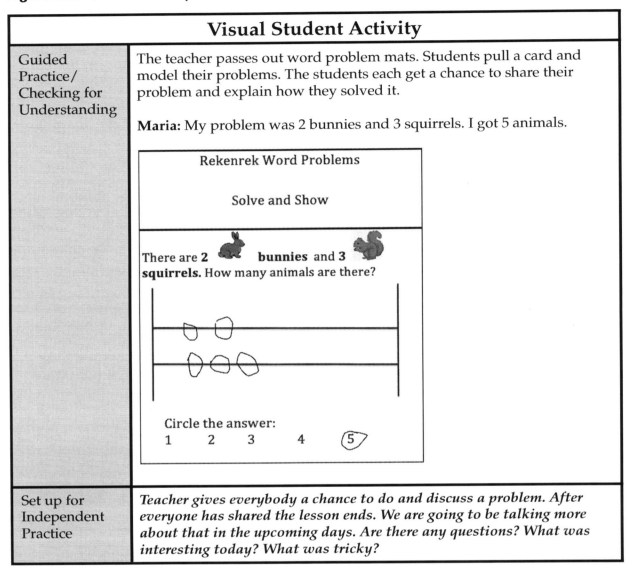

	Visual Student Activity
Guided Practice/ Checking for Understanding	The teacher passes out word problem mats. Students pull a card and model their problems. The students each get a chance to share their problem and explain how they solved it. **Maria:** My problem was 2 bunnies and 3 squirrels. I got 5 animals.
Set up for Independent Practice	*Teacher gives everybody a chance to do and discuss a problem. After everyone has shared the lesson ends. We are going to be talking more about that in the upcoming days. Are there any questions? What was interesting today? What was tricky?*

Figure 6.26 Lesson Close

Close
♦ What did we do today? ♦ What was the math we were practicing? ♦ Was this easy or tricky? ♦ Turn to a partner and state one thing you learned today.

Figure 6.27 Rekenrek Recording Paper

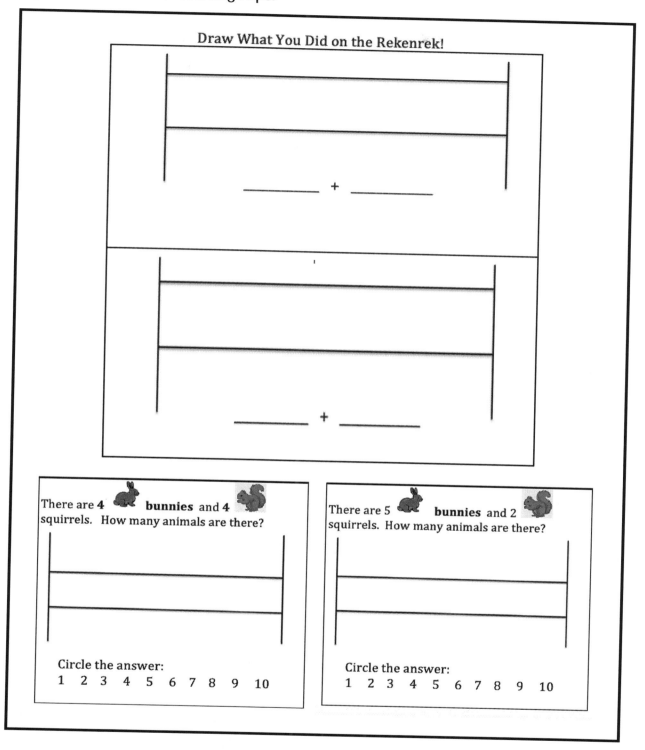

Draw What You Did on the Rekenrek!

_____ + _____

_____ + _____

There are **4** bunnies and 4 squirrels. How many animals are there?

Circle the answer:
1   2   3   4   5   6   7   8   9   10

There are 5 bunnies and 2 squirrels. How many animals are there?

Circle the answer:
1   2   3   4   5   6   7   8   9   10

Figure 6.28

There are 3 🐰 **bunnies** and 3 🐿 
squirrels. How many animals are there?

There are 5 🐰 **bunnies** and 5 🐿 
squirrels. How many animals are there?

There are 3 🐰 **bunnies** and 2 🐿 
squirrels. How many animals are there?

Abstract Lesson

Figure 6.29 Abstract Introduction

	Introduction Exploring with Abstract Activities
Launch	**Teacher:** Today we are going to continue to work on solving word problems. **Vocabulary:** part-part whole, whole, part, word problem, count up, number sentence (equation) **Math Talk:** The whole is _____. One part is _____. The other part is _____.
Model	**Teacher:** Today we are going to play a match game. We have to find the word problem, the part-part whole diagram and the number sentence that all match. There are 3 problems that are all mixed up in the bags. I am going to let you work with your partner to talk and discuss the problems and match them up. I am going to listen and ask you questions. Let's do 1 together. 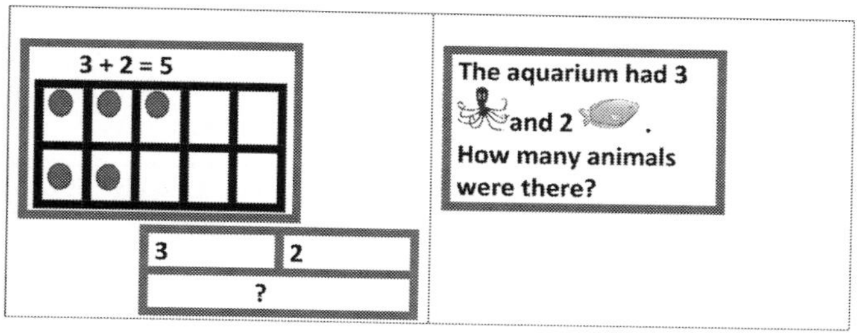 **Teacher:** Does everybody see this model. Who can explain it? **Ted:** There are 3 octopi and 2 fish. There are 5 animals. The part-part whole mat has those numbers. **Kelly:** The ten frame also shows that!
Checking for Understanding	**The students talk about 1 more problem as a group and then they work with partners.**

Figure 6.30 Student Activity

	Abstract Student Activity
Guided Practice/ Checking for Understanding	The teacher watches the students as they work together to discuss and match the problems. **Teacher watches Leah and Tom.** How do you know this ten frame goes with the problem? **Leah:** Because it says 4 + 3 and that shows 4 plus 3. **David:** The part-part whole mat shows 4 + 3 also. 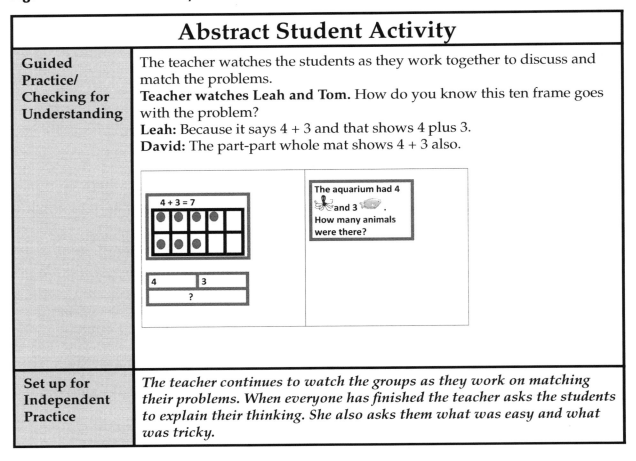
Set up for Independent Practice	*The teacher continues to watch the groups as they work on matching their problems. When everyone has finished the teacher asks the students to explain their thinking. She also asks them what was easy and what was tricky.*

Figure 6.31 Lesson Close

Close
♦ What did we do today? ♦ What was the math we were practicing? ♦ Was this easy or tricky? ♦ Turn to a partner and state one thing you learned today.

Figure 6.32 Word Problem Matches

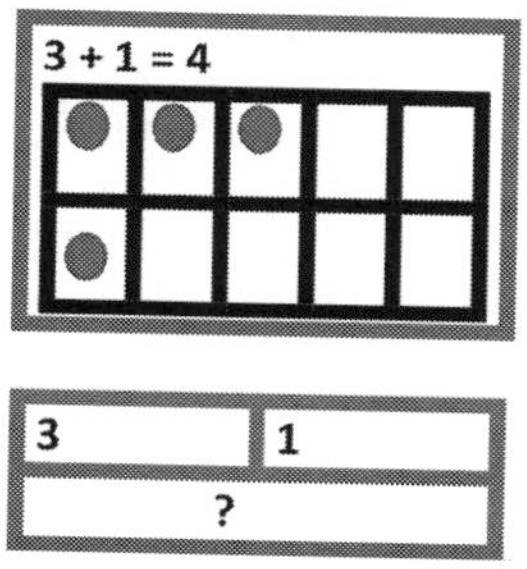 3 + 1 = 4 3 | 1 ?	The aquarium had 3  🐙 and 1  🐟. How many animals were there?
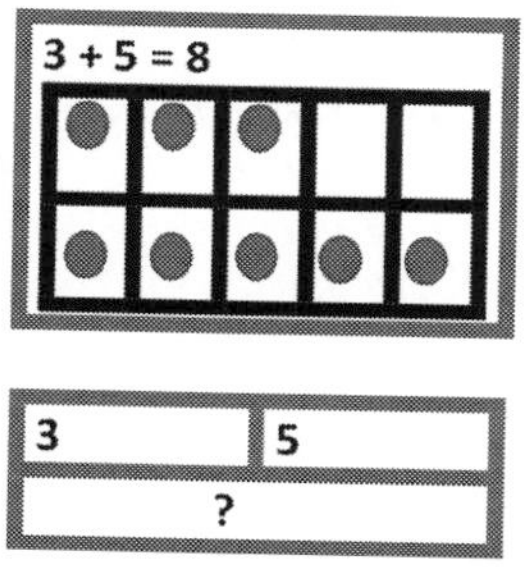 3 + 5 = 8 3 | 5 ?	The aquarium had 3  🐙 and 5  🐟. How many animals were there?
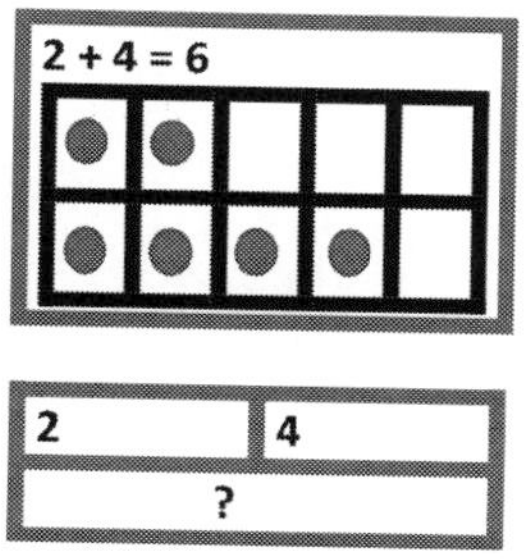 2 + 4 = 6 2 | 4 ?	The aquarium had 2  🐙 and 4  🐟. How many animals were there?
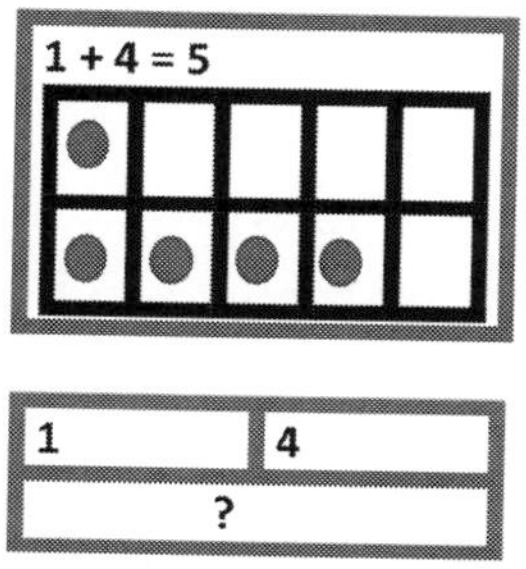 1 + 4 = 5 1 | 4 ?	The aquarium had 1  🐙 and 4  🐟. How many animals were there?
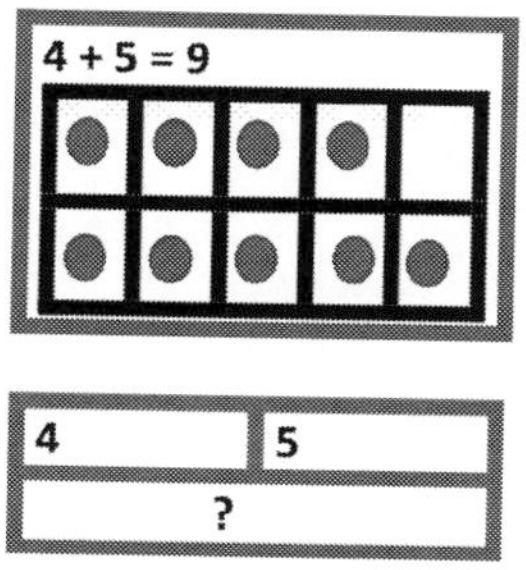 4 + 5 = 9 4 | 5 ?	The aquarium had 4  🐙 and 5  🐟. How many animals were there?

Section Summary

Part-part whole problems are rather easy for students. Be sure to use the templates and have the students act them out. Make a big life-size part-part whole mat so that students can act out the problem in it. Also make a big number bond that students can stand in. Often, people use hula hoops to do this. The point is that you need students to see how the parts come together. In their problem solving toolkits students should have these templates as well.

Overview

Figure 6 33 Overview

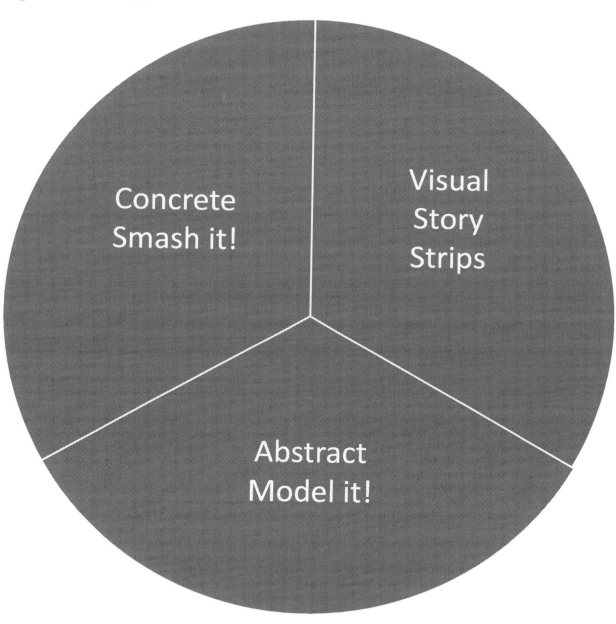

Concrete
Smash it!

Visual
Story
Strips

Abstract
Model it!

Figure 6.34 Planning Template

Take From Word Problems	
Big Idea: There are different types of word problems. In this type, we are taking from. **Enduring Understanding:** We can model problems in many ways. **Essential Question:** What are the ways to model this type of problem? **I can statement:** I can model part-part whole word problems.	**Materials** ♦ Tools: Cubes ♦ Templates: Ten Frame ♦ Cards ♦ Crayons
Cycle of Engagement **Concrete:** ●●●　　●● **Visual: Drawing** ○○○　∅∅ **Abstract: Mental Number line** | 1 | 2 | 3 | 4 | 5 | 6 | 7 | 8 | 9 | 10 |	Vocabulary & Language Frames ♦ Count Up ♦ Count Back ♦ Addends ♦ Difference _____ take away ____ is _____.
Questions: How did you solve that? Are you sure you are correct? Did you double check your answer? Did you solve one way and check another	**Math Processes/Practices** ♦ Problem Solving ♦ Reasoning ♦ Models ♦ Tools ♦ Precision

Figure 6.35 Differentiation

Three Differentiated Lessons

In this series of lessons, students are working on the concept of take away problems. They are developing this concept through concrete activities, visual activities and abstract activities. Everybody should do the cycle. Some students progress through it more quickly than others. Here are some things to think about as you do these lessons.

Emergent	On Grade Level	Above Grade Level
Review subtraction. As you introduce this to students, do a lot of work by acting it out and then doing it with manipulatives. Be sure to have students draw what they acted out and connect it to number models.	The grade level standard is that students can model it and explain it. So do lots of this work where students are modeling it and explaining it. Also show and talk about exemplars and non-exemplars of this concept.	Use more formal word problem structures and larger numbers.

 Looking for Misunderstandings and Common Errors

Subtraction is more difficult than addition. Students should spend a great deal of time acting out the problems. Have the students act the problems out in life-size five and ten frames. They should also use the subtraction machine that is described in this chapter. The reason is it is a graphic organizer helping students to understand the process of taking away. Be sure to make sure students can count back and count up. Practice these skills often.

Figure 6.36 Anchor Chart

Solving Take Away Problems

Jane has 5 rings. She gave her sister 2 rings. How many does Jane have left?

Five Frame:

5 − 2 = ?

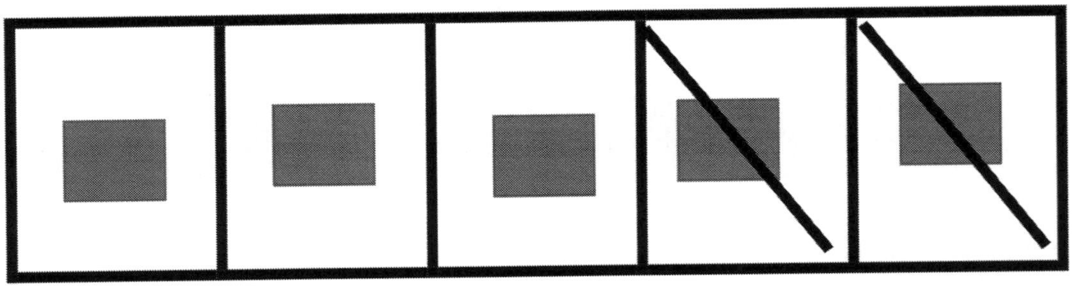

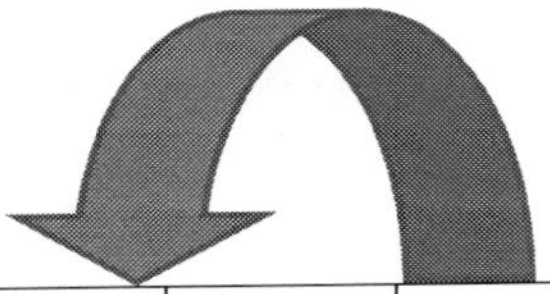

Number Path

| 1 | 2 | 3 | 4 | 5 | 6 | 7 | 8 | 9 | 10 |

Sketch

Concrete Lesson

Figure 6.37 Concrete Introduction

Introduction
Exploring with concrete activities

Launch	**Teacher:** Today we are going to work on take away problems. We are going to solve them with counters. **Vocabulary:** take away, subtract, minus sign, difference **Math Talk:** _____ take away ____ is _____.
Model	Teacher gives each student a baggie of counters. Teacher explains activity: We are going to tell stories and act them out with our counters. **Teacher:** Listen to this problem. Jamal had 7 marbles. 5 rolled away. **Teacher:** Ok. How many are left? **Tom:** 7 take away 5 is 2. The difference is 2. **Teacher:** Who has question for Tom? **Marta:** How do you know? Prove it! **Tom:** I put 7 on my ten frame and I took 5 away. I have 2 left. See: 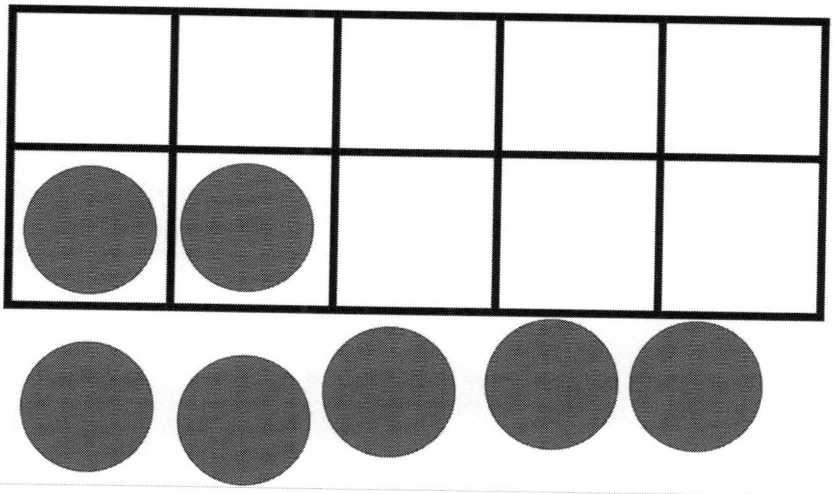 **Teacher:** Great question Marta. Great reasoning Tom. **Teacher:** Here's another problem:

(Continued)

Figure 6.37 (Continued)

	Michael had 8 marbles. 3 rolled away. **Teacher:** Ok. Who can explain what happened? Think about your math words. 8 take away 3 is 5. The difference is 5. **Timothy:** Michael had 8 marbles. 3 rolled away. **Teacher:** 3 what? **Timothy:** Marbles. **Teacher:** Ok, explain what you did. **Timothy:** I put 8 marbles out and then I took away 3. There are 5 left. **Teacher:** Who agrees and why? **Yessenia:** I agree. I got 5 too. See I did it on my fingers (she holds up 8 fingers and takes away 3 and shows that there are 5 left). 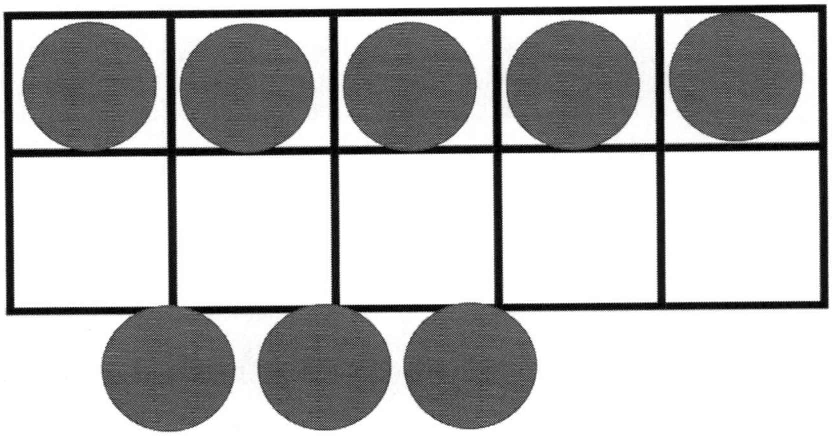 *Teacher reads 2 more problems that the group discusses*
Checking for Understanding	**Teacher:** Ok. I am going to give each one of you your own problem. I want you to read it. Solve it. Be ready to share how you did it. I am going to watch you and if you need help, look at our anchor charts, ask a math partner and of course you can ask me.

Figure 6.38 Student Activity

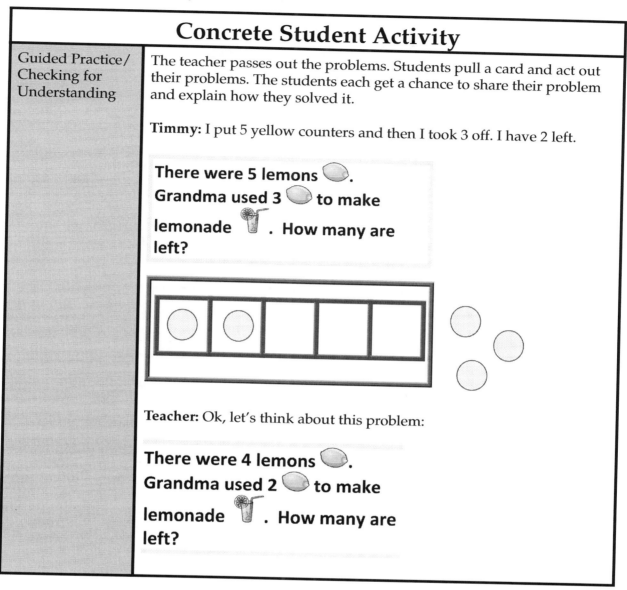

Concrete Student Activity

| Guided Practice/ Checking for Understanding | The teacher passes out the problems. Students pull a card and act out their problems. The students each get a chance to share their problem and explain how they solved it. |

Timmy: I put 5 yellow counters and then I took 3 off. I have 2 left.

There were 5 lemons.
Grandma used 3 to make
lemonade. How many are
left?

Teacher: Ok, let's think about this problem:

There were 4 lemons.
Grandma used 2 to make
lemonade. How many are
left?

(Continued)

Figure 6.38 (Continued)

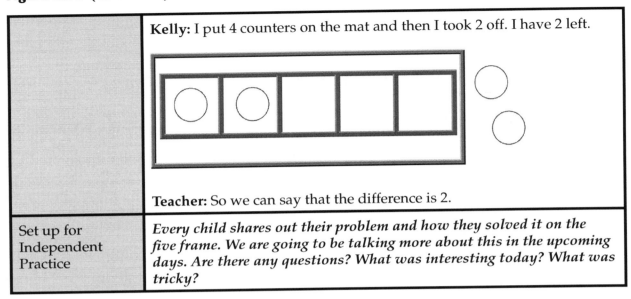

	Kelly: I put 4 counters on the mat and then I took 2 off. I have 2 left. Teacher: So we can say that the difference is 2.
Set up for Independent Practice	*Every child shares out their problem and how they solved it on the five frame. We are going to be talking more about this in the upcoming days. Are there any questions? What was interesting today? What was tricky?*

Figure 6.39 Lesson Close

Close
♦ What did we do today?   ♦ What was the math we were practicing?   ♦ Was this easy or tricky?   ♦ Turn to a partner and state one thing you learned today.

Visual Lesson

Figure 6.40 Visual Introduction

<table>
<tr>
<td colspan="2" align="center"><h2>Introduction
Exploring with Visual Activities</h2></td>
</tr>
<tr>
<td>Launch</td>
<td>Teacher: Today we are going to work on telling take away word problems. I am going to give you a word problem strip. You will look at the storytelling strip and tell the take away problem.

Vocabulary: take away, subtract, minus sign

Math Talk: _____ take away ____ is _____.</td>
</tr>
<tr>
<td>Model</td>
<td>Teacher: Look at these story telling strips. Who can tell a take away story using them?

Marta: There were 7 lemons. Grandma used 2 to make lemonade. There are 5 left.

Teacher: Excellent story. Who has a question for Marta?

Hong: Can you prove it another way?

Marta: Yes, with my fingers. (She holds up 7 and takes away 2. She says "see there are 5 left."

Raul: I am going to tell one. There were 8 lemons. Grandma used 4 to make lemonade. There are 4 left.</td>
</tr>
<tr>
<td>Checking for Understanding</td>
<td>

Teacher: Great!
Students continue to tell stories.</td>
</tr>
</table>

Figure 6.41 Student Activity

Visual Student Activity

Guided Practice/ Checking for Understanding	The teacher passes out different picture cards. Students pull a card and tell their problems. The students each get a chance to share their problem and explain how they solved it. **Maria:** My problem is this. There were 4 monkeys and 3 left. Now there is 1 monkey. 
Set up for Independent Practice	*Teacher gives everybody a chance to do and discuss a problem. After everyone has shared the lesson ends. We are going to be talking more about this in the upcoming days. Are there any questions? What was interesting today? What was tricky?*

Figure 6.42 Lesson Close

Close

- What did we do today?
- What was the math we were practicing?
- Was this easy or tricky?
- Turn to a partner and state one thing you learned today.

Figure 6.43 Storytelling Strips (Editor Note: This is all 1 figure)

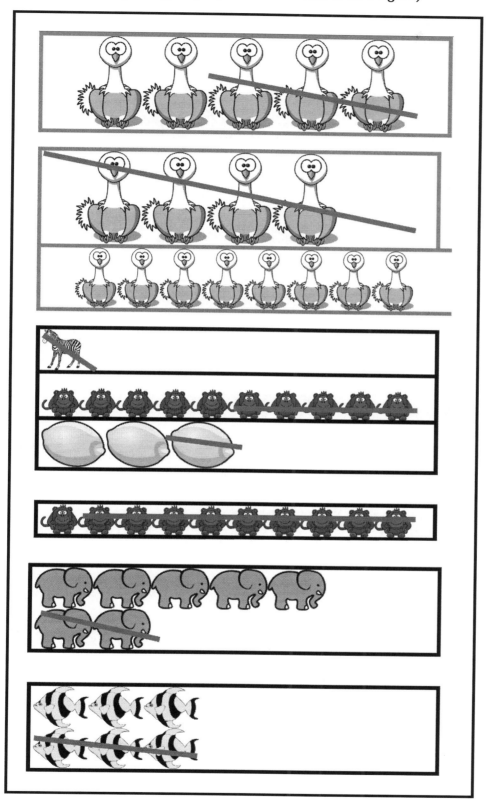

Abstract Lesson

Figure 6.44 Abstract Introduction

Introduction
Exploring with Abstract Activities

Launch	**Teacher:** Today we are going to work on solving take away word problems. Here we have word problems on a card. **Teacher:** Let's look at our math talk chart: **Vocabulary:** take away, subtract, minus sign **Math Talk:** _____ take away _____ is _____.
Model	**Teacher:** We are going to tell word problems and then match the number sentence. Who's ready? Who thinks they can find the number sentence that matches this picture?  **Todd:** This one $$7 - 1 = 6$$ **Teacher:** Yes. How do you know? **Todd:** Because there are 7 elephants and 1 left. So there is 6. **Teacher:** Who wants to go next? **Kelly:** I do. There were 6 fish and 3 swam away. So there are 3. **Teacher:** Is there another way she could model it to check? **Chris:** Yes, on her fingers. See 6 take away 3 is 3.

$$6 - 3 = 3$$

Checking for Understanding	The teacher continues to discuss the picture problems and the equations with the group. Then, students work in pairs to find the models and the equations.

Figure 6.45 Student Activity

Abstract Student Activity

Guided Practice/ Checking for Understanding	**Teacher:** Today we are going to work on word problems. You and your partner are going to find the picture card and tell the story to each other and then find the number sentence that matches. I am going to ask you all questions as you do it. **Teacher:** Elijah, tell me the story of your card? **Elijah:** There were 4 birds. They all flew away. How many are left. ZERO!  **Teacher:** Fantastico! What number sentence matches that story? **Carol:** 4–4 is 0. **Teacher:** Why? **Carol:** Because if you have 4 (she holds up her fingers) and you take all of them away… there is nothing left.
Set up for Independent Practice	The teacher continues to watch the groups as they work on solving their problems. When everyone has finished the teacher asks the students to explain their thinking. She also asks them what was easy and what was tricky?

Figure 6.46 Lesson Close

Close

- ◆ What did we do today?
- ◆ What was the math we were practicing?
- ◆ Was this easy or tricky?
- ◆ Turn to a partner and state one thing you learned today.

Figure 6.47 Storytelling Strips and Equations

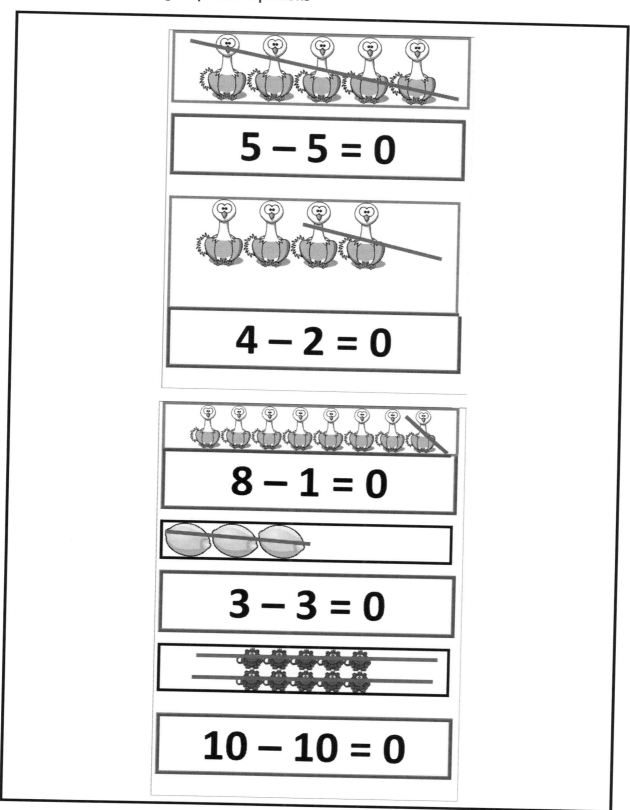

Figure 6.47 (Continued)

$$7 - 2 = 5$$

$$6 - 3 = 3$$

Section Summary

Take away problems are tricky. Students have trouble with subtraction and so they often struggle with subtraction problems. Make sure you have number paths and number ladder so students can act out the problems. They should solve the problems and tell the stories. Students should have various tools in their toolkits like number paths, counting charts, subtraction machine mats and more. They should use various tools such as cubes, tiles and bears to model and explain their thinking. They should also discuss their strategies.

Part-Part Whole Both Addends Unknown

Overview

Figure 6.48 Overview

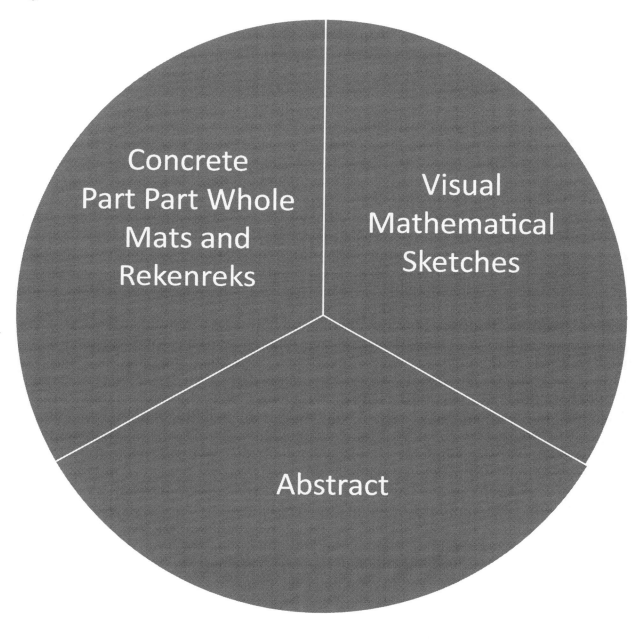

Figure 6.49 Planning Template

Exploring Place Value with Place Value Blocks

Big Idea: There are different types of word problems. Today we are looking at both addend unknown problems.

Enduring Understanding: We can model problems in many ways.

Essential Question: What are the ways to model this type of problem?

I can statement: I can model word problems.

Materials
- Tools: Cubes
- Templates: Ten Frame
- Cards
- Crayons

Questions
- How do you know?
- Are you sure?
- Did you solve more than 1 way?
- Did you check your answer?
- Does your answer make sense?

Cycle of Engagement

Concrete: Place Value Blocks

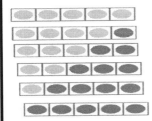

Visual: Drawing

*Braining Camp Virtual Manipulatives

Vocabulary & Language Frames

- Addends
- Sum

Abstract: Mental Number line
5 + 0
4 + 1
3 + 2
2 + 3
1 + 4
4 + 1
0 + 5

Figure 6.50 Differentiation

Three Differentiated Lessons

In this series of lessons, students are working on the concept of *part-part whole both parts unknown* word problems. They are developing this concept through concrete activities, visual activities and abstract activities. Everybody should do the cycle. Some students progress through it more quickly than others. Here are some things to think about as you do these lessons.

Emergent Level	On Grade Level	Above Grade Level
As you introduce this to students, do a lot of work by acting it out and then doing it with manipulatives. Be sure to have students draw what they acted out and connect it to number models.	The grade level standard is that students can model it and explain it. So do lots of this work where students are modeling it and explaining it.	Once they get the concept, increase the number range.

 Looking for Misunderstandings and Common Errors

These types of problems are very tricky for students. It is important to act these out with the students, for example doing boy and girl problems. There were four students. Some were boys, and some were girls. How many of each could there be? The students should stand up and act it out. There could be all boys or 3 boys and 1 girl, 2 boys and 2 girls, 1 boy and 3 girls, or 4 girls.

Figure 6.51 Anchor Chart

Solving Part-Part Whole Problems

On the tree there are butterflies and beetles. There are 5 altogether. How many of each could there be?

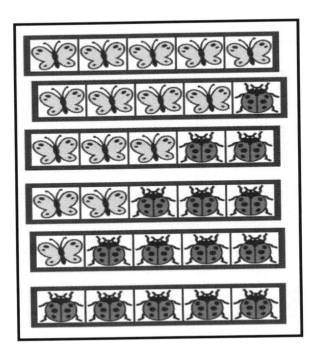

Math learning center virtual ten frames

Concrete Lesson

Figure 6.52 Concrete Introduction

Introduction
Exploring with Concrete Activities

Launch	**Teacher:** Let's talk about this story. **Vocabulary:** addends, both, some,
Model	**Teacher:** Listen to the problem. Mike has 4 marbles. Some are blue and some are red. How many could there be of each? Math Learning Center
Checking for Understanding	*Teacher reads 2 more problems that the group discusses.* **Teacher:** Ok. I am going to give each one of you your own problem. I want you to read it. Solve it. Be ready to share how you did it. I am going to watch you and if you need help, look at our anchor charts and of course you can ask me.

Figure 6.53 Student Activity

	Concrete Student Activity
Guided Practice/ Checking for Understanding	The teacher passes out the problems. Students pull a card and act out their problems. The students each get a chance to share their problem and explain how they solved it. **Marta:** My problem is this: Mike has 3 marbles. Some are blue and some are gray. 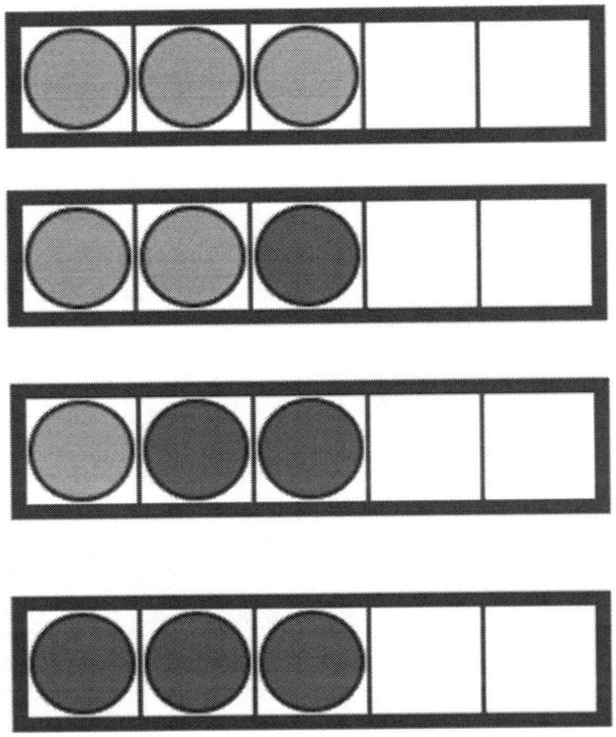 So, I put 3 blue and then 2 and then 1 and then it is a pattern…
Set up for Independent Practice	*Every child shares out their problem and how they solved it. We are going to be talking more about this in the upcoming days. Are there any questions? What was interesting today? What was tricky?*

Figure 6.54 Lesson Close

Close
◆ What did we do today? ◆ What was the math we were practicing? ◆ Was this easy or tricky? ◆ Turn to a partner and state one thing you learned today.

Figure 6.55 Both Addends Word Problem Cards

Mike has 4 marbles. Some are red and some are yellow. How many could there be of each?	Marta has 5 marbles. Some are red and some are yellow. How many could there be of each?
Mary has 3 marbles. Some are red and some are yellow. How many could there be of each?	Mina has 2 marbles. Some are red and some are yellow. How many could there be of each?
Joe has 6 marbles. Some are red and some are yellow. How many could there be of each?	Jenny has 7 marbles. Some are red and some are yellow. How many could there be of each?
Jamal has 8 marbles. Some are red and some are yellow. How many could there be of each?	Grace has 9 marbles. Some are red and some are yellow. How many could there be of each?

Visual Lesson

Figure 6.56 Visual Introduction

<table>
<tr>
<td colspan="2" align="center"><h2>Introduction
Exploring with Visual Activities</h2></td>
</tr>
<tr>
<td>Launch</td>
<td>

Teacher: Today we are going to continue to work on part-part whole problems.

Vocabulary: more than, less than, equal to, the same as, whole, word problem, count up, number sentence (equation)

Math Talk: The pattern is _____.

</td>
</tr>
<tr>
<td>Model</td>
<td>

Teacher: Here is my story. Missy had some circles and some triangles. She had 5 shapes altogether. How many could she have had of each? Watch me model my thinking with sketches on the five frames

Teacher: Does everybody see this model? Who can explain it?
Ted: You drew all the ways.

Teacher: So what is the first way I could have it?

Marta: First all circles.

Lucas: Then 4 circles and 1 triangle.

Mike: Then 3 circles and 2 triangles.

Kelly: Then 2 circles and 3 triangles.

Jamal: Then 1 circle and 4 triangles.

Michael: Then 0 circles and 5 triangles.

Tracie: It's a pattern!

Teacher: Does everyone see that pattern? It is a way to show how to break apart the number 5.

Marta: I want to try one.

</td>
</tr>
<tr>
<td>Checking for Understanding</td>
<td>

This conversation continues with the students using the *five frames to sketch their thinking about both addends unknown stories.*

</td>
</tr>
</table>

Figure 6.57 Student Activity

Visual Student Activity

Guided Practice/ Checking for Understanding	The teacher passes out word problem cards. Students pull a card and model their problems. The students each get a chance to share their problem and explain how they solved it.
	Maria: My problem is this:
	Mike has 3 marbles. He has red and yellow. What are the different combinations that he could have?
	I know... all yellow, 2 yellow and 1 red or 1 yellow and 2 red or 3 red... It's easy. It's a pattern. See.
	It's easy to color in.
	Teacher: Does everybody see how she did that. She modeled it on her grid and then she drew it. She can explain what she did.
Set up for Independent Practice	*Teacher gives everybody a chance to do and discuss a problem. After everyone has shared the lesson ends.*
	We are going to be talking more about this in the upcoming days. Are there any questions? What was interesting today? What was tricky?

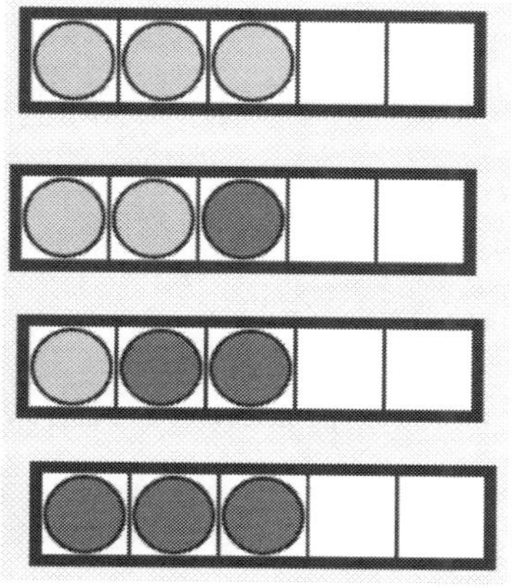

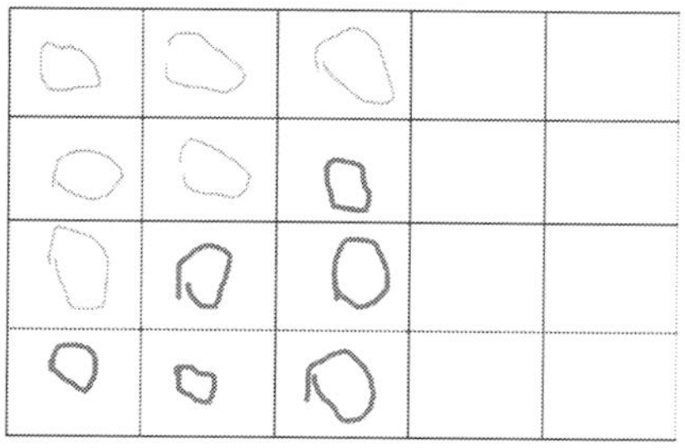

Figure 6.58 Lesson Close

Close
♦ What did we do today?
♦ What was the math we were practicing?
♦ Was this easy or tricky?
♦ Turn to a partner and state one thing you learned today.

Visual Lesson

Figure 6.59 Abstract Introduction

<table>
<tr>
<td colspan="2" align="center"><h2>Introduction
Abstract Exploration</h2></td>
</tr>
<tr>
<td>Launch</td>
<td>Teacher: Today we are going to keep working on word problems. Let's look at this one. There are 2 different color markers. There are 4 markers. Some are green and some are yellow. What do you notice?

Vocabulary: addends, part-part whole, word problem, pattern

Math Talk: The pattern is _____.</td>
</tr>
<tr>
<td>Model</td>
<td>Teacher: Today we are going to solve some more word problems. This time we are going to act them out and then write the numbers in a table. But today there is a twist to our problem. You have to have some of each color. Who wants to describe the story we see here.

Ray-Ray: There were 4 markers. 3 were green and 1 was yellow.

Teacher: Very good. So see how they have that in the table. Ok, what is another way we could have the markers.

Taylor: 2 green and 2 yellow. Ok, see how they have that in the table also.

Mike: We could also have 1 green and 3 yellow. See how they have that in the table too.

UNIT **4**: MODELING THE PROBLEMS

Way#1: Try drawing pictures to help!

Green Markers   Yellow Markers

Way# 2: Using the Table technique.

MARKER COMBINATION	
Green	Yellow
3	1
2	2
1	3

Problem Solving with Math Models© 2019   69</td>
</tr>
<tr>
<td>Checking for Understanding</td>
<td>Teacher: Do you see a pattern?
Tim: Yes 3 and then 2 and then 1.
Teacher: Yes that is on one side. What about the other?
Kelli: It goes 1 and then 2 and then 3.</td>
</tr>
</table>

Figure 6.60 Student Activity

Abstract Student Activity

Guided Practice/ Checking for Understanding	**Teacher:** Ok, everybody take out your crayons. We are going to do this one together. It says Betty has 4 hats. Some are yellow and some are pink. What could we draw? There has to be some of each kind.

PUT TOGETHER/TAKE APART-BOTH ADDENDS UNKNOWN

1. Betty has 4 hats. Some hats are yellow and some hats are pink. How many hats could be yellow? How many hats could be pink? What are all the possible combinations, if there are some of each?

Way#1: Draw pictures

Way#2: Solve with a table

HATS	
Yellow	**Pink**
3	
2	
1	

Teacher: Who can tell me what to do first?

Lisa: First we draw 3 yellow and 1 pink.
Maite: Then, 2 yellow and 2 pink.
Carlos: 1 yellow and 3 pink.
James: It's a pattern again!
Teacher: Explain how it is a pattern.
Lisa: It goes 3 and then 2 and then 1…
Maite: We need to write the numbers to match.

Set up for Independent Practice	**The teacher continues working with the group on different problems.** Each time, they discuss it and complete the pictures and the table. When everyone has finished the teacher asks the students to explain their thinking. She also asks them what was easy and what was tricky.

Figure 6.61 Lesson Close

Close
♦ What did we do today?
♦ What was the math we were practicing?
♦ Was this easy or tricky?
♦ Turn to a partner and state one thing you learned today.

Section Summary

Both addend unknown problems are often tricky for students through second grade. One of the best ways to tackle these problems is to act them out and talk about the pattern. By physically acting it out, drawing it and then connecting the table representation, students can begin to understand the idea of decomposing a number in different ways. It is important for students to talk about the pattern and to learn how to organize the pattern in a way that they see all the combinations.

3 Read Problems

Figure 6.62 3 Read Problems Planning Template

3 Read Problems	
Big Idea: We can use different strategies and models to solve word problems. **Enduring Understanding:** We can model problems in many ways. **Essential Question:** What are the ways to model this type of problem? **I can statement:** I can use tools to model my thinking.	**Materials** ♦ Tools: Cubes ♦ Templates: Ten Frame ♦ Cards ♦ Crayons
Cycle of Engagement **Concrete-Visual-Abstract** In this type of problem, the class chorally reads the problem 3 times. The first time the class reads the problem, they focus on what is happening in the problem. The second time they focus on what the numbers mean. The third time they focus on asking questions about the problems.	**Vocabulary & Language Frames** Strategies Models Tools

Figure 6.63 Anchor Chart

---

3 Read Word Problem

We can read a problem 3 times.

The first time we read it and think about the situation.
What is the story about? Who is in it? What is happening?

The second time we read it and think about the numbers.
What are the numbers? What do they mean? What might we do with those numbers in this situation?

The third time we read it and think about what questions we could ask.
What do we notice in this story? What do we wonder? What do we want to ask about this story?

Jamal had 5 marbles. His brother had 2.

First Read: What is this story about? It is about a guy and his brother and their marbles.
Second Read: What do the numbers mean? Jamal has 5. His brother has 2.

Third Read: What could we ask about this story?
How many do they have altogether?
How many more does Jamal have than his brother?
How many fewer marbles does his brother have than he does?
How many more would his brother need to have the same amount as he does?

Figure 6.64 3 Read Word Problems

	3 Read Word Problems Lesson **I CAN solve word problems.**
Launch	**Teacher:** Today we are going to work on word problems. We are going to do a 3 read, like the ones we do in whole group. **Vocabulary:** model, strategy, **Math Talk:** The whole is _____. One part is _____. The other part is
Model	**Story: The bakery had 10 cookies. They had 7 chocolate chip and 3 lemon ones.** *First Read: What is this story about?* *It is about the bakery. They have different types of cookies.* *Second Read: What do the numbers mean?* *They have 7 chocolate chip cookies and 3 lemon ones.* *Third Read: What could we ask about this story?* *How many cookies were there altogether?* *How many more chocolate chip cookies did they have than lemon ones?* *How many fewer lemon cookies do they have than chocolate chip cookies?*
Checking for Understanding	**Teacher:** Ok, pick 1 question and answer it. We will come back in a few minutes to discuss them…. Who answered question 1? Tell us your strategy and show us a model of your thinking. *Timothy: I did how many do they have altogether? I added it up on the rekenrek.*

Guided Practice/ Checking for Understanding	Teacher: Ok, who did it another way? Eric: I did it on the ten frame. 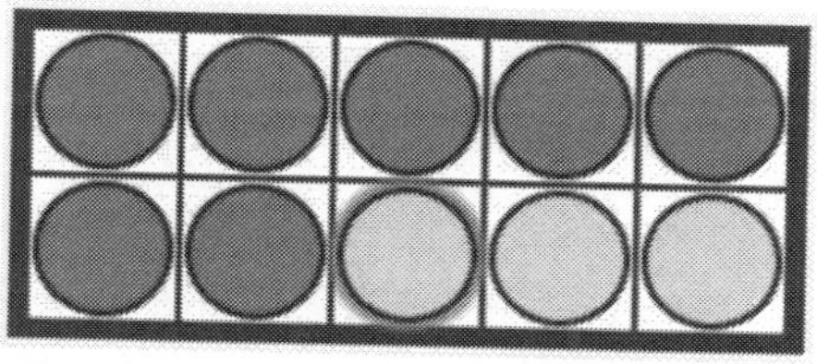
Set up for Independent Practice	*Students continue to share their thinking with the group. When they are done the teacher facilitates a conversation about what the math was for the day and then what students thought was easy and what they thought was tricky.*

Figure 6.65 Lesson Close

Close
◆ What did we do today? ◆ What was the math we were practicing? ◆ Was this easy or tricky? ◆ Turn to a partner and state one thing you learned today.

Figure 6.66 3 Read Cards

Marta had 3 red marbles and 2 orange marbles.	The store had 2 red apples and 3 green apples.
Kelly had 4 blue rings and 2 orange rings.	The jewelry store had 5 bracelets and 5 rings.
Maite had 2 blue rings and 2 orange rings.	The jewelry store had 1 bracelet and 4 rings.

Picture Prompt Word Problems

Figure 6.67 Picture Prompt Word Problems Planning Template

Picture Prompt Word Problems

Big Idea: Word problems are a part of our everyday lives. **Enduring Understanding:** We can model problems in many ways. There are many different strategies to solve them. **Essential Question:** What are the ways to model problems? **I can statement:** I can model problems.	**Materials** ♦ Tools: Cubes ♦ Templates: Ten Frame ♦ Cards ♦ Crayons
	Questions ♦ What is your strategy? ♦ What is your model? ♦ Why does that work? ♦ How can you show that?

Cycle of Engagement **Concrete:** **Visual: Drawing** **Abstract:: Match Addends and the Sum** 2 + 5 7	**Vocabulary & Language Frames** **My strategy was …** **My model was …**

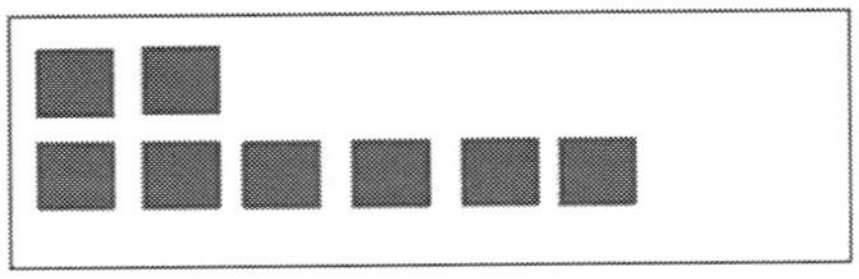

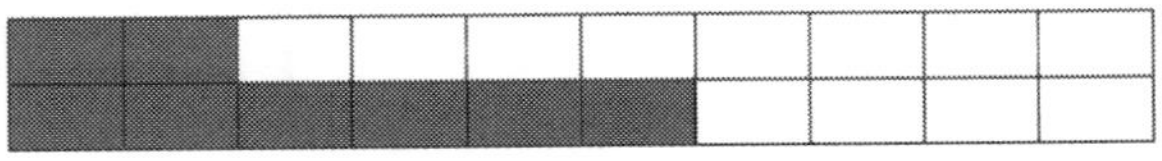

Figure 6.68 Picture Prompt Word Problem Introduction

Picture Prompt Word Problems

Launch	**Teacher:** Today we are going to tell word problems. **Vocabulary:** Add, Subtract, Word problems
Model	**Teacher:** Today we are going to look at pictures and tell word problems. We are working mainly on addition and subtraction stories. Here is a picture. Who can tell me a story about these donuts. 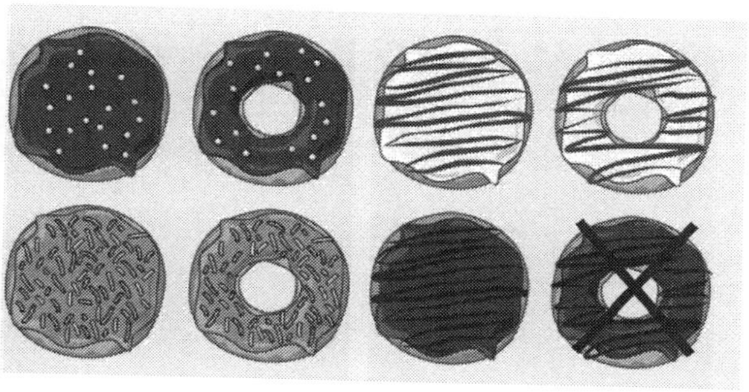 **Lara:** There were 8 donuts. My mom took one. **Teacher:** Ok, that works! What could be our number sentence. **Marta:** I know. 8 take away 1. That makes 7! **Teacher:** Let's look at our tools. Is there a way we could model this problem with one of them. **Kelly:** Yes, on the number line you could go to 8 and then jump back 1.
Checking for Understanding	**Teacher:** Ok. Great thinking. Does someone have another way? **Todd:** Yes, I did it on my fingers...see 8 take away 1 is 7.
Guided Practice/ Checking for Understanding	Teacher continues to discuss different ways and then shows another picture.
Set up for Independent Practice	After a few discussions, the teacher asks what was easy and what was tricky and if there are any questions. Then, the students go to their workstations.

Section Summary

It is important to do open questions with students where they have to contextualize numbers. This is part of the mathematical practices and processes (CCSSM, 2010). We want students to be able to reason about numbers. We want students to be able to tell stories about addition and subtraction. Giving them rich structures to do that is vital.

Depth of Knowledge

Depth of Knowledge is a framework that encourages us to ask questions that require that students think, reason, explain, defend and justify their thinking (Webb, 2002). Here is a snapshot of what that can look like. It is important to continually reflect on what the level of the lesson is. In working in small groups on problem solving, be sure to ask open questions so that students can think and reason out loud with others.

Figure 6.69 Depth of Knowledge

	What are different strategies and models that we can use to solve addition problems?	What are different strategies and models to model subtraction problems?	What are different strategies and models that we can use to model part-part whole problems?
DOK Level 1 (These are questions where students are required to simply recall/reproduce an answer/do a procedure.)	Solve: There were 2 dogs and 3 more came. How many dogs are there now?	Solve: There were 5 dogs, and 2 left. How many dogs are there now?	Solve: There were 2 dogs and 3 cats. How many animals are there altogether?
DOK Level 2 (These are questions where students have to use information, think about concepts and reason.) This is considered a more challenging problem than a level 1 problem.	Model this problem in two different ways. There were 3 dogs, and 2 more came. How many dogs are there now? Explain your thinking. Model the problem in two different ways.	Model this problem in two different ways. There were 5 dogs, and 4 left. How many dogs are there now? Explain your thinking. Model the problem in two different ways.	Model this problem in two different ways. There were 2 dogs and 2 cats. How many animals are there altogether? Explain your thinking.
DOK Level 3 (These are questions where students have to reason, plan, explain, justify and defend their thinking.)	Solve. Tell me an addition story. Defend your answer. Prove that it is correct by solving one way and checking another.	Solve. Tell me a subtraction story. Defend your answer. Prove that it is correct by solving one way and checking another.	Tell me a story about dogs and cats. Solve and model the problem in two different ways.

Figure 6.70 Asking Rigorous Questions

DOK 1	DOK 2 **At this level students explain their thinking.**	DOK 3 **At this level students have to justify, defend and prove their thinking with objects, drawings and diagrams.**
What is the answer to ??? Can you model the problem? Can you identify the answer that matches this equation?	How do you know that the equation is correct? Can you pick the correct answer and explain why it is correct? How can you model that problem in more than one way? What is another way to model that problem? Can you model that on the. . . . ??? Give me an example of a . . . type of problem. Which answer is incorrect? Explain your thinking.	Can you prove that your answer is correct? Prove that . . . Explain why that is the answer. Show me how to solve that and explain what you are doing.

Resources

A great resource for asking open questions is Marion Small's *Good Questions: Great ways to differentiate mathematics instruction in the standards-based classroom* (2017). Also, Robert Kaplinsky has done a great job in pushing our thinking forward with the Depth of Knowledge Matrices he created (https://robertkaplinsky.com/depth-knowledge-matrix-elementary-math/). Kentucky Department of Education (2007) also has a great example of DOK math matrices.

Key Points

- Add to result unknown problems
- Part-part whole problems
- Take from result unknown problems
- Part-part whole both addends unknown
- 3 read problems
- Picture prompt word problems

Chapter Summary

It is important to work with students in small guided math groups focusing on word problems. Word problems have a learning trajectory (Carpenter, Fennema, Franke, Levi, & Empson, 1999/2015). Most states have outlined the word problem types that each grade level is responsible for in their standards. So, in a guided math group, the goal is to work with students around the word problem types that they are learning.

Students are usually at different levels when learning word problems. They are scaffolded into a hierarchy that goes from easy to challenging. In most states, kindergarten students are responsible for about four different add/subtraction problem types altogether.

The small group discussion should reference the whole group problem solving work. The focus should be on getting students to think about the context and the numbers, to reason about the problem and use visual representations and tools to unpack it. In kindergarten, students should also work on matching expressions and equations to problems. In first grade the focus becomes writing expressions and equations, although some kindergarteners are ready to do this too!

Reflection Questions

1. How are you currently teaching word problems?
2. Are you making sure that you do concrete, visual and abstract activities?
3. What do your students struggle with the most, and what ideas are you taking away from this chapter that might inform your work around those struggles?

References

Carpenter, T. P., Fennema, E., Franke, M. L., Levi, L., & Empson, S. B. (1999/2015). *Children's Mathematics: Cognitively Guided Instruction*. Portsmouth, NH: Heinemann.

CCSSM. (2010). Retrieved May 15, 2021 from http://www.corestandards.org/Math/

Kentucky Department of Education. (2007). *Support Materials for Core Content for Assessment Version 4.1 Mathematics*. Retrieved January 15, 2017 from the internet.

Schoenfeld, A. H. (1991). On Mathematics as Sense-Making: An Informal Attack on the Unfortunate Divorce of Formal and Informal Mathematics. In J. F. Voss, D. N. Perkins, & J. W. Segal (Eds.), *Informal Reasoning and Education* (pp. 311–343). Hillsdale, NJ: Lawrence Erlbaum Associates.

Small, M. (2017). *Good Questions: Great Ways to Differentiate Math in the Standards Based Classroom*. New York: Teachers College Press.

Stacey, K., & MacGregor, M. (1999). Learning the Algebraic Method of Solving Problems. *The Journal of Mathematical Behavior*, 18(2), 149–167. https://doi.org/10.1016/S0732-3123(99)00026-7

Webb, N. (2002). An Analysis of the Alignment Between Mathematics Standards and Assessments for Three States. Paper presented at the *Annual Meeting of the American Educational Research Association*. New Orleans, LA.

7

Counting and Cardinality

Counting and cardinality is a major topic in kindergarten. Students should spend a great deal of time working on different types of activities that build number sense. In this chapter we will focus on four key topics: number representation, subitizing, composing and decomposing numbers, and comparing numbers. In kindergarten, students are expected to represent numbers within 20. In guided math groups, we must make sure that we are giving students time to explore the numbers concretely with counters, Play-Doh and tools. As they work with the manipulatives, they build it and then draw it and then name it.

Subitizing helps students with unitizing, counting on, composing and decomposing numbers as well as adding and subtracting (Clements, 1999). Subitizing has been found to be a "strong indicator of students' mathematical abilities" (Desoete, Ceulemans, Roeyers, & Huylebroeck, 2009). Working with students on subitizing improves their subitizing ability. It is important when working in small groups to pull students in their zone of proximal development. Some students are working on subitizing objects within 4 and 5, while others are subitizing within 7 or 10.

Most if not all state standards require that students know how to compose and decompose numbers. Composing and decomposing is an essential skill in mathematics (Ma, 1999). In this chapter we will look at a variety of ways to work on composing and decomposing numbers within 10. Richardson (1997) maintained that it is important that students have lots of practice with small numbers, instead of jumping to big numbers too quickly.

Comparing numbers is always tricky. There are 19 levels on the learning trajectory for learning to compare numbers. Students should go through a cycle of concrete, pictorial and abstract learning (Clements, 2019). According to most state standards, when learning to compare numbers, students should match, then count and then just know it.

Research Note 🔍

♦ The research shows that what happens in early childhood is a predictor of what happens later on in elementary through high school and life (Jordan, Kaplan, Ramineni, & Locuniak, 2008, 2009; Locuniak & Jordan, 2008).

♦ Counting is complex and teachers should understand and intentionally teach not just basic but the advanced concepts of counting early (Geary et al., 2017; Nguyen et al., 2016).

♦ "Subitizing is a fundamental skill in the development of students' understanding of number" (Baroody 1987, 115).

DOI: 10.4324/9781003169529-7

In this chapter we will explore:

♦ Counting
♦ Subitizing
♦ Composing and decomposing numbers
♦ Comparing numbers

Counting

Overview

Figure 7.1 Overview

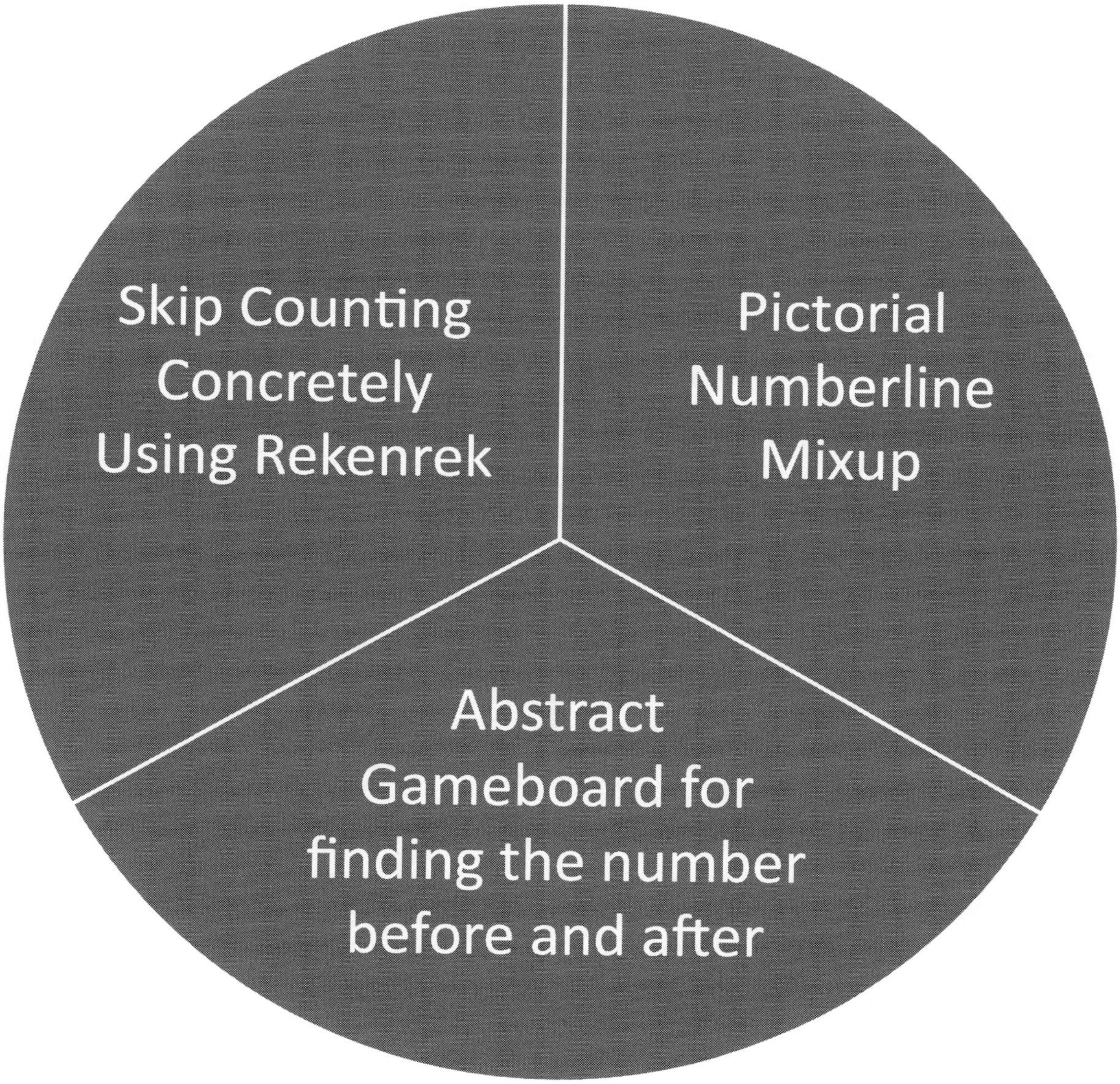

Figure 7.2 Planning Template

Counting

Big Idea: Counting involves many different skills **Enduring Understanding:** Students will understand what it means to skip count, sequence numbers and find the number before and after **Essential Question:** What are the ways to count and represent items to 20? **I can statement:** I can count amounts to 20. I know numbers that come before and after a number. I know how to skip count by 10's.	**Cycle of Engagement** **Concrete: Say it, See it and build it**

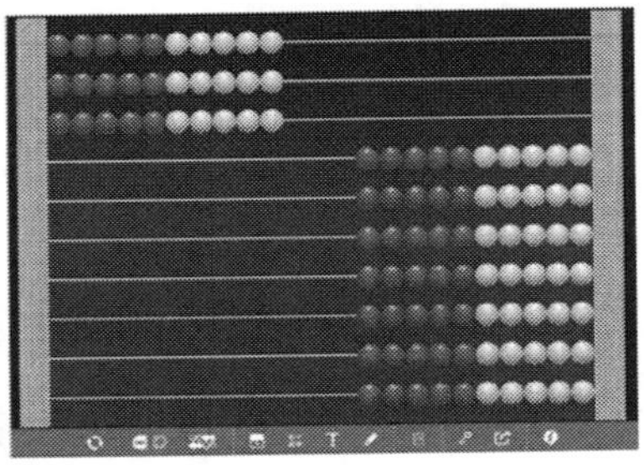

Materials
- Tools: Cubes
- Templates: Ten Frame
- Cards
- Crayons

Pictorial:

1	2	3	4	5	6	7	8	9	10

Abstract: Find the number before and after

12	11	9	7
8	6	2	10
5	10	11	4
4	12	5	6
1	3	8	2

Questions
- What did we do today?
- What was the math we were practicing?
- Was this easy or tricky?
- Are there any questions?

Vocabulary & Language Frames
- Addends
- Sum

___ and ___ make _____

The sum of ___ and ____ is _____

Processes/Practices
- Focus on reasoning
- Communicating thinking
- Modeling the Math
- Using Tools
- Thinking about pattern
- Looking for and making use of structure

Figure 7.3 Differentiation

Three Differentiated Lessons		
In this series of lessons, students are working on different concepts of counting using different types of models. They are developing these concepts through concrete activities, pictorial activities and abstract activities. Here are some things to think about as you do these lessons.		
Emerging	**On Grade Level**	**Above Grade Level**
Students have to understand skills for numbers within 10 and then work on those same concepts for numbers greater than 10.	Use different models to represent these concepts and skills.	Expand the number range.

 Looking for Misunderstandings and Common Errors

When students are first learning to count, they are shaky. When they are skip counting by 10's often they are just chanting. It is important to show them what they are doing with physical things. In the next part of this section, we work on looking at the number before and the number after. So, make sure they can count with cardinality before you start looking for the number before and the number after. These are the beginning levels of counting and this will take a while. Students do not really get proficient at identifying the number before and after without counting from 1 until the higher levels of counting. They learn how to do this within 10 and then within 20.

Figure 7.4 Anchor Chart

Working with Numbers

Concrete: We can skip count by 10's

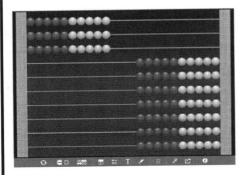

Pictorial: We can order numbers in the correct sequence

1	2	3	4	5	6	7	8	9	10

Abstract: We can point to a number and say the number before and after

12	11	9	7
8	6	2	10
5	10	11	4
4	12	5	6
1	3	8	2

Concrete Lesson

Figure 7.5 Concrete Introduction

	Introduction Concrete Exploration
Launch	**Teacher:** Today we are going to work on counting by 10's. When we are counting by tens we are actually like fast counting items. We are going to use our rekenreks to look at this. **Vocabulary:** count by 10's, rekenrek, **Math Talk:** 10, 20, 30 etc.
Model	**Teacher:** You each have your virtual rekenreks. We are going to look at what it means to count by 10's. Watch me. Listen to me count as I move over ten…. 10, 20, 30…. Do you see and hear how I am moving over 10 at a time and counting. 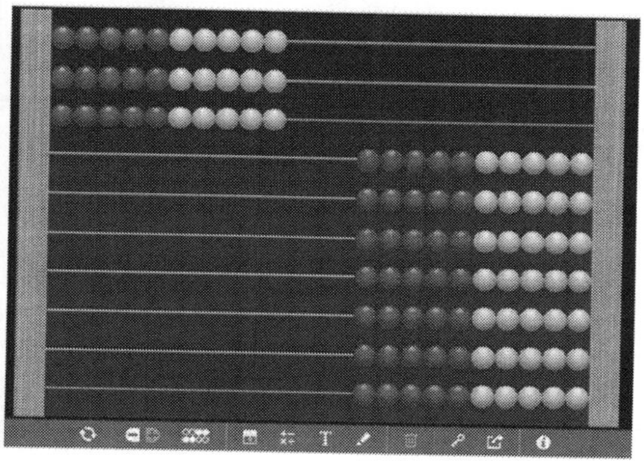 **Teacher:** Ok who wants to try doing it. **David:** I do: 10,20,30,40,50 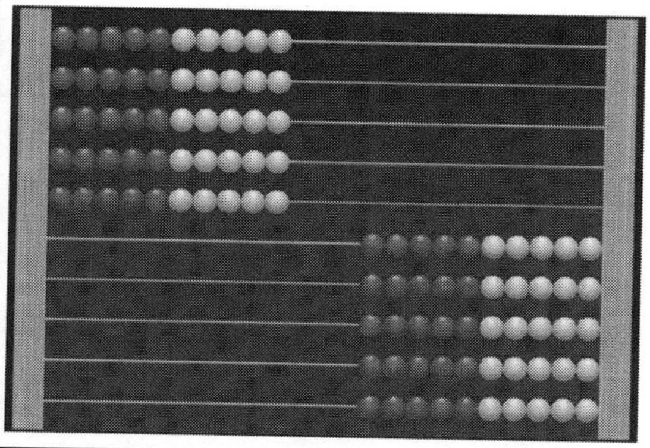 ….
Checking for Understanding	**Teacher:** Ok, we are all going to get a chance to do it.

Figure 7.6 Student Activity

Student Concrete Activity	
Guided Practice/ Checking for Understanding	**Teacher:** Who wants to start? **Kelli:** I do. It's easy. 10,20,30,40,50,60,70 etc.... 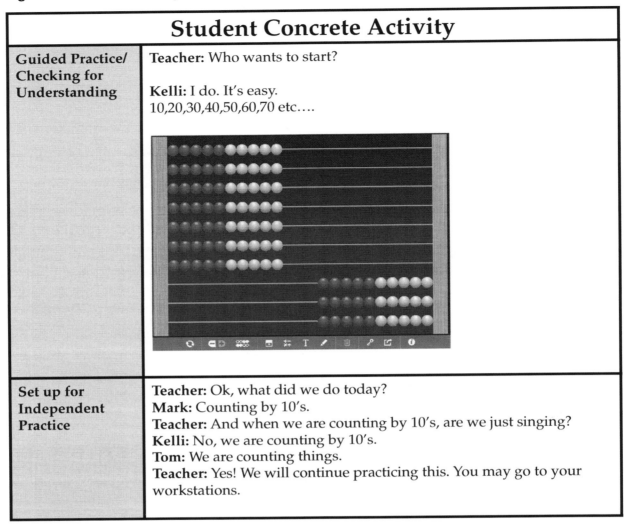
Set up for Independent Practice	**Teacher:** Ok, what did we do today? **Mark:** Counting by 10's. **Teacher:** And when we are counting by 10's, are we just singing? **Kelli:** No, we are counting by 10's. **Tom:** We are counting things. **Teacher:** Yes! We will continue practicing this. You may go to your workstations.

Figure 7.7 Lesson Close

Close
◆ What did we do today? ◆ What was the math we were practicing? ◆ Was this easy or tricky? ◆ Turn to a partner and state one thing you learned today.

Visual Lesson

Figure 7.8 Visual Introduction

	Introduction Visual Exploration
Launch	**Teacher:** Today we are going to count and work on naming the number that comes before another number. **Vocabulary:** before, after, in between **Math Talk:** _____ comes before _____. _____ comes after _____.
Model	**Teacher:** Today we are going to continue working on counting in order and naming the number before a number. I have all these numbers. They are all mixed up. Who can help me? 5 9 7 8 1 6 4 10 3 2
Checking for Understanding	**Teacher:** Now you all are going to pull a card and say the number that comes before the number. Then, look at the number line and check it. 1 2 3 4 5 6 7 8 9 10

Figure 7.9 Student Activity

Student Visual Activity	
Guided Practice/ Checking for Understanding	Students go around the table and each of them pull a card and name the number that comes before it. Their partner holds a number path and checks. The teacher listens, takes notes and asks questions. **Kayla:** 6. I picked 7 and the number 6 comes before 7. I counted… 1,2,3,4,5,6 and then 7 **Maite:** Yes. She is right. I checked it on the number path. `1  2  3  4  5  6  7  8  9  10`
Set up for Independent Practice	**Teacher:** Ok, what were we doing today? **Maite:** Looking for numbers on the number line. **Teddy:** Before and after. **Teacher:** How does the number line help us? **Raul:** You can see the numbers.

Figure 7.10 Lesson Close

Close
◆ What did we do today? ◆ What was the math we were practicing? ◆ Was this easy or tricky? ◆ Turn to a partner and state one thing you learned today.

Abstract Lesson

Figure 7.11 Abstract Introduction

	Introduction Abstract Exploration
Launch	**Teacher:** Today we are going to work on looking at and finding numbers that come before other numbers. **Vocabulary: model, addend, sum, total** **Math talk:** _____ comes before _____.
Model	**Teacher:** Pull a card and the person with the largest number goes first. Cover the number that comes before the number you pulled. You can look at the number path to help you. Each person should have their own color markers. Whoever covers 3 in a row wins. | 12	11	9	7
8	6	2	10
5	10	11	4
4	12	5	6
1	3	8	2	 | 1 | 2 | 3 | 4 | 5 | 6 | 7 | 8 | 9 | 10 | 11 | 12 | | 2 | | 4 | | 7 | | 9 |
Checking for Understanding	**Teacher:** Does everybody understand how to do it? Who can give me an example? **Yesenia:** Like if I pull 2 then I have to cover 1 because it comes before 2. **Teacher:** Ok, does everybody see what she did? Ok, let's start.

Figure 7.12 Student Activity

	Student Abstract Activity
Guided Practice/ Checking for Understanding	Students play the game with a partner. Their partner holds a number path and checks. The teacher listens, takes notes and asks questions. **Kayla:** 7. I picked 9 and the number 8 comes before 9. **Maite:** Yes. She is right. I checked it on the number path. | 1 | 2 | 3 | 4 | 5 | 6 | 7 | 8 | 9 | 10 |
Set up for Independent Practice	**Teacher:** Great. The number path can help you double check. You could also double check by counting in your head. What was the math that we were doing today? **Marvin:** Working on telling the number before. **Teacher:** We are going to continue working on this in the next few days. You can all go to your workstations.

Figure 7.13 Lesson Close

Close
◆ What did we do today? ◆ What was the math we were practicing? ◆ What were we doing with our number paths? ◆ Was this easy or tricky? ◆ Turn to a partner and state one thing you learned today.

Figure 7.14 Playing Cards

6	2	3	4	5
6	7	8	9	10
11	12	13	10	11

Figure 7.15 Game Mat

12	**11**	**9**	**7**
8	**6**	**2**	**10**
5	**10**	**11**	**4**
4	**12**	**5**	**6**
1	**3**	**8**	**2**

Figure 7.16 Blank Game Mat

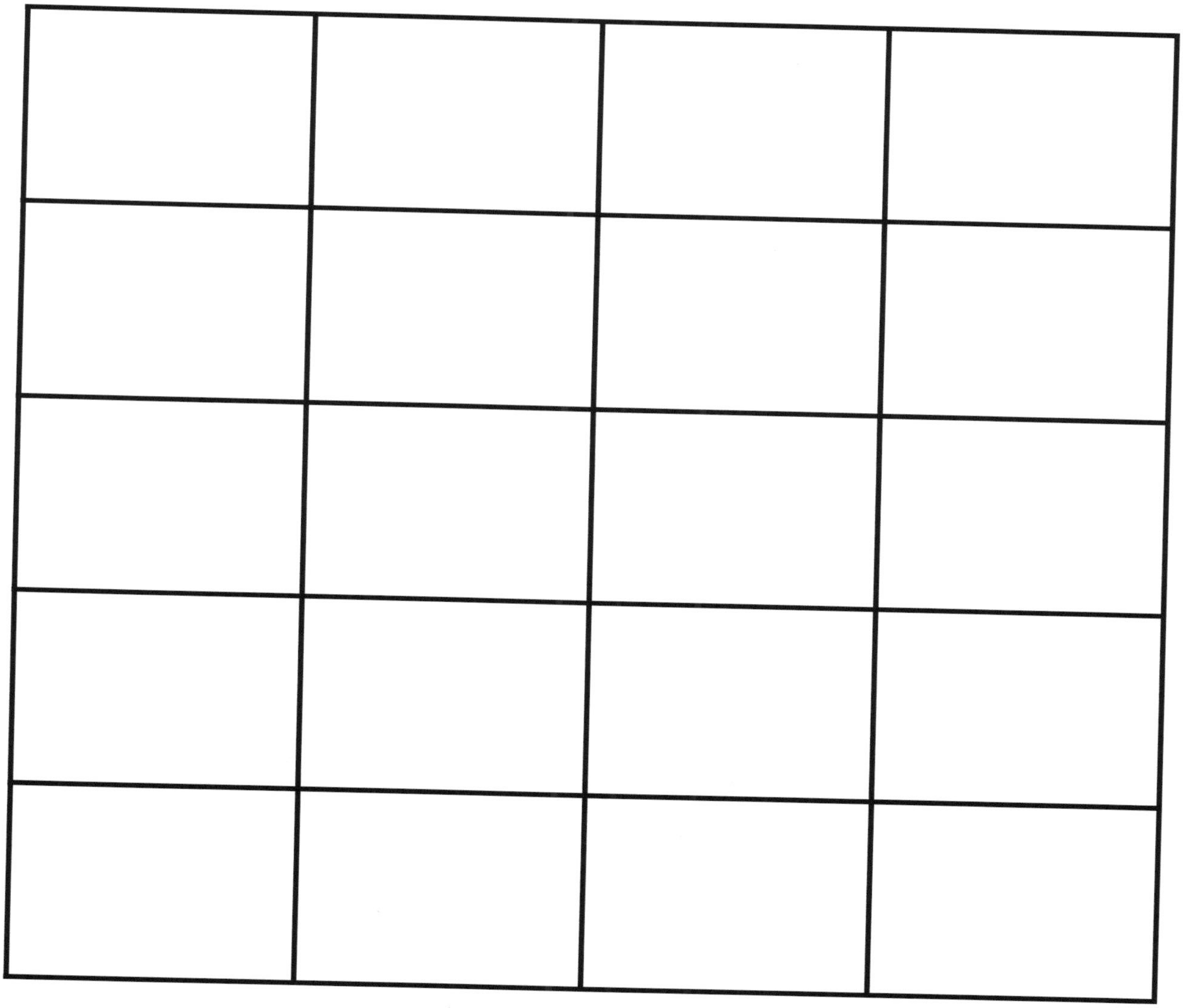

Section Summary

Teaching students to count with understanding is really important and foundational. We often get students to rote count without understanding, and we have to really shift this thinking and work towards students to be able to understand the math they are doing and able to explain it. So, when learning counting, students shouldn't just be engaging in rote out loud exercises but be able to see those numbers in action. So, a great example of this is to use the hundred grid so the students can see the numbers when counting to 100. Also use number lines and especially growing ones . . . ones that add the numbers as you get to them in the kindergarten class. Students should also keep track of their own growing hundred grids and number lines as well (see Jmeacham calendar activities). When skip counting by 10's make sure students are connecting this activity to some visuals. When working with what number comes before and after and in between make sure they have visual references. All of these things help to cement the knowledge.

Subitizing

Overview

Figure 7.17 Overview

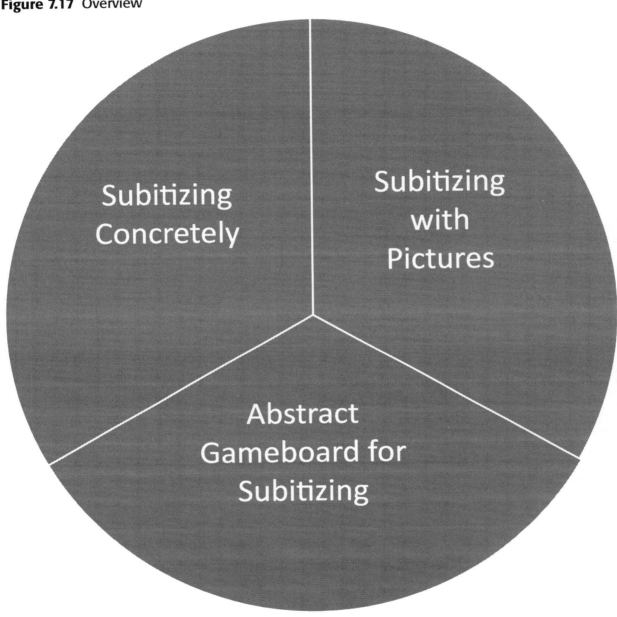

Figure 7.18 Planning Template

Subitizing

Big Idea: Knowing an amount without counting

Enduring Understanding: Students will understand and be able to subitize within 10

Essential Question: Why should we know how to subitize? How does it help us to see patterns?

I can statement: I can know some amounts without counting.

Cycle of Engagement

Concrete: See it and say it.

Pictorial:

ROLL AND COVER

Abstract:

Materials
◆ Tools: Cubes
◆ Templates: Ten Frame
◆ Cards
◆ Crayons

Questions
◆ What did we do today?
◆ What was the math we were practicing?
◆ Was this easy or tricky?
◆ Are there any questions?

Vocabulary & Language Frames
◆ Addends
◆ Sum
___ and ___ make _____
The sum of ___ and ____ is _____

Processes/Practices
◆ Focus on reasoning
◆ Communicating thinking
◆ Modeling the Math
◆ Using Tools
◆ Thinking about pattern
◆ Looking for and making use of structure

Figure 7.19 Differentiated Lessons

Three Differentiated Lessons
In this series of lessons, students are working on the concept of subitizing using different types of models. They are developing this concept through concrete activities, pictorial activities and abstract activities. Here are some things to think about as you do these lessons.

Emerging	On Grade Level	Above Grade Level
Review counting.	Use different models to represent expressions and equations.	Expand the number range.

 Looking for Misunderstandings and Common Errors

Subitizing is the foundation of arithmetic. You should start doing it at the beginning of kindergarten. There are actually ten levels of subitizing. In kindergarten students usually work between levels 4 and 7 (Clements and Sarama, www.learningtrajectories.org). At level 4 students are working on the perceptual level where they are looking at and saying the amount. At level 5 they are beginning to conceptually subitize by breaking apart numbers and can talk about them in ways such as 2 and 3 make 5. At level 6 they can do this all the way to 20. At level 7 students start looking at amounts through place value and skip counting. In kindergarten they can begin to see and talk about groups of 2 or 3, etc.

Figure 7.20 Anchor Chart: Subitizing

Cycle of Engagement

Concrete: See it and say it.

Pictorial: Look and Know it!

ROLL AND COVER

Abstract: Ten Frame Flash!

Concrete Lesson

Figure 7.21 Concrete Introduction

Introduction Concrete/Visual Explorations

Launch	**Teacher:** Today we are going to roll a dice and say how many dots we see. **Vocabulary:** subitize, count, say it **Math Talk:** I see …..
Model	**Teacher:** Ok, I am going to show you a dice. You tell me what you see.  **Ted:** I see 1 on one dice.  **Terry:** I see 3. **Teacher:** Are you sure? **Ted:** Yes there is only 1 dot. **Terry:** There are 3… she points 1,2,3,
Checking for Understanding	**Teacher:** Ok, we are all going to get a chance to do it.

Figure 7.22 Student Activity

Student Concrete Activity	
Guided Practice/ Checking for Understanding	**Teacher:** Who wants to start? **Kelli:** I do. It's easy. I see 9. There are 5 on top and 3 on the bottom. **Tom:** I see 8? **Teacher:** Let's all double check. **Kelli:** It's 8. **Teacher:** It's always good to double check. 
Set up for Independent Practice	**Teacher:** Ok, what did we do today? **Mark:** We worked on looking without counting. **Teacher:** And when we you see it you say it. **Tom:** We are counting things. **Teacher:** Yes! We will continue practicing this. You may go to your workstations.

Figure 7.23 Lesson Close

Close
♦ What did we do today? ♦ What was the math we were practicing? ♦ What were we doing with our dice and subitizing? ♦ Was this easy or tricky? ♦ Turn to a partner and state one thing you learned today.

Visual Lesson

Figure 7.24 Visual Introduction

Introduction Visual Explorations

Launch	**Teacher:** Today we are going to roll a dice and say how many pips we see. Then we are going to draw it. **Vocabulary:** subitize, count, say it **Math Talk:** I see …..
Model	**Teacher:** Ok, I am going to show you a dice. You tell me what you see. And then you are going to draw it on your template. **Marta:** I see 6. I drew 6. 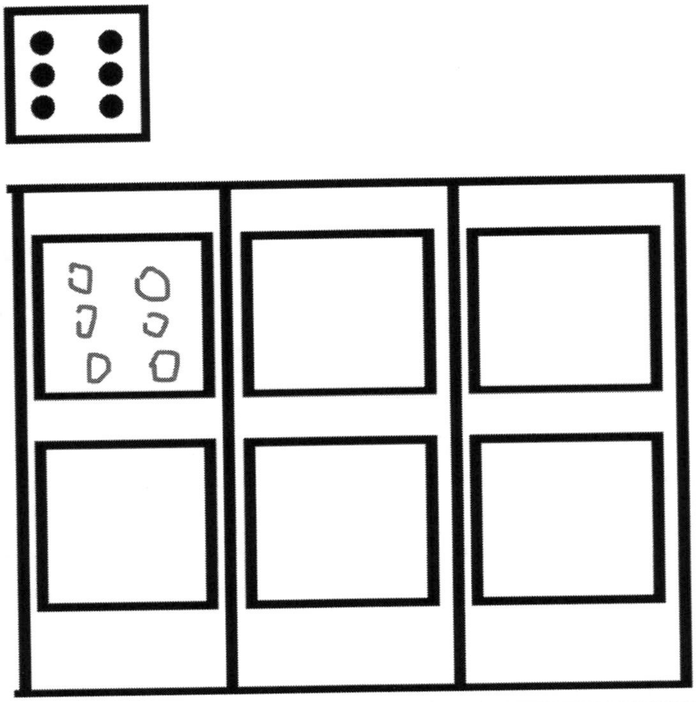
Checking for Understanding	**Teacher:** Ok, we are all going to get a chance to do it.

Figure 7.25 Student Activity

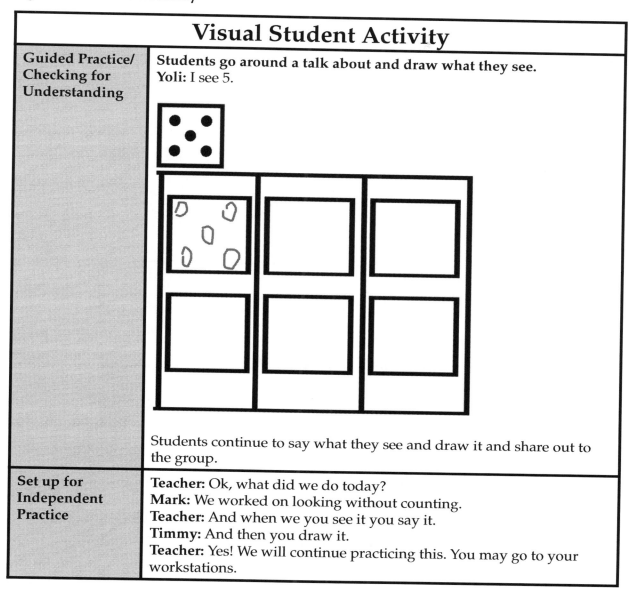

	Visual Student Activity
Guided Practice/ Checking for Understanding	Students go around a talk about and draw what they see. **Yoli:** I see 5. Students continue to say what they see and draw it and share out to the group.
Set up for Independent Practice	**Teacher:** Ok, what did we do today? **Mark:** We worked on looking without counting. **Teacher:** And when we you see it you say it. **Timmy:** And then you draw it. **Teacher:** Yes! We will continue practicing this. You may go to your workstations.

Figure 7.26 Lesson Close

Close

- ♦ What did we do today?
- ♦ What was the math we were practicing?
- ♦ What were we doing with our dice and subitizing?
- ♦ Was this easy or tricky?
- ♦ Turn to a partner and state one thing you learned today.

Abstract Lesson

Figure 7.27 Abstract Introduction

Introduction Abstract Explorations	
Launch	**Teacher:** Today we are going to roll a dice and say how many dots we see. **Vocabulary:** subitize, count, say it **Math Talk:** I see …..
Model	**Teacher:** Today you are going to take turns rolling dice. You will subitize the amount and then find it and cover it on the board. You will work together to try and get the whole board covered.  **ROLL AND COVER!**
Checking for Understanding	**Teacher:** Ok, you will each work with a partner.

Figure 7.28 Student Activity

Abstract Student Activity

Guided Practice/ Checking for Understanding	Students go around and talk about and draw what they see. **Yoli:** I see 5. I covered 5. **Tom:** I see 4. I covered 4.  Students continue playing with their partners.
Set up for Independent Practice	**Teacher:** Ok, what did we do today? **Mark:** We worked on looking without counting. **Teacher:** And when we you see it you say it. **Timmy:** And then you cover it on the board. **Teacher:** Yes! We will continue practicing this. You are going to have this game in your workstations.

Figure 7.29 Lesson Close

Close
◆ What did we do today?
◆ What was the math we were practicing?
◆ What were we doing with our dice and subitizing?
◆ Was this easy or tricky?
◆ Turn to a partner and state one thing you learned today.

Section Summary

Subitizing is a very important skill that kindergarteners need to know. It is important to teach it throughout the year. This should be a daily routine so that students can get really strong with this skill. Teachers need to practice subitizing in lots of different ways. Students should subitize with ten frames, dice, dominos, dots and cube wands. Check out my subitizing board on Pinterest.

Composing and Decomposing Numbers

Overview

Figure 7.30 Overview

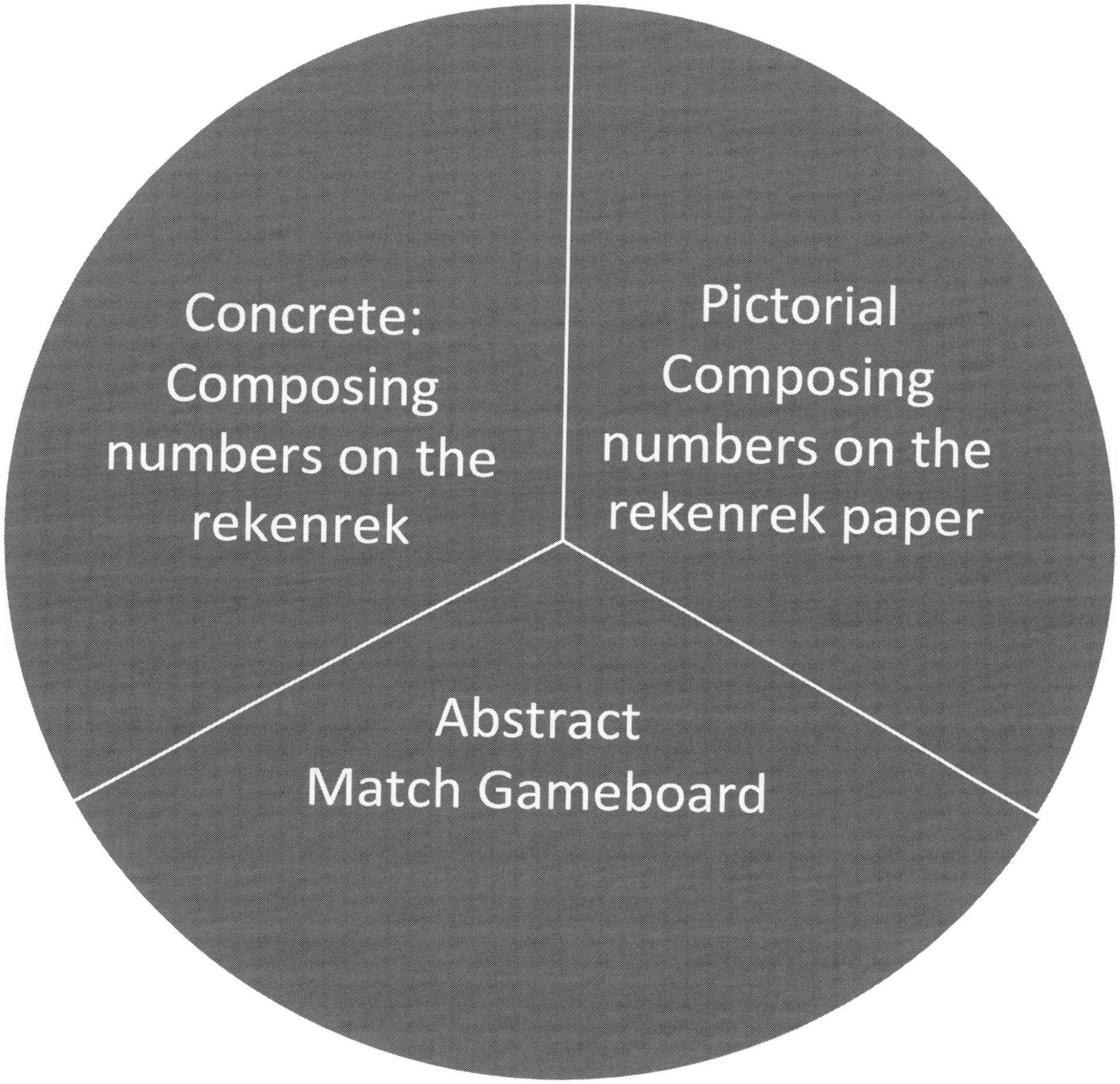

Concrete: Composing numbers on the rekenrek

Pictorial Composing numbers on the rekenrek paper

Abstract Match Gameboard

Figure 7.31 Planning Template

Composing Numbers

Big Idea: There are certain number combinations that make 7

Enduring Understanding: Students will understand and be able to recall the number combinations to 7.

Essential Question: What are the ways to make 7?

I am learning to statement: I am learning to make 7 in different ways.

Materials
- Tools: Cubes
- Templates: Ten Frame
- Cards
- Crayons

Questions
- What did we do today?
- What was the math we were practicing?
- Was this easy or tricky?
- Are there any questions?

Vocabulary & Language Frames
- Make 7
- Addends
- Sum
- ___ and ___ make _____

Cycle of Engagement

Concrete: Compose numbers on the Rekenrek

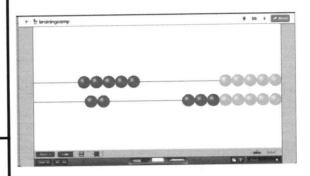

Pictorial: Record work on the Rekenrek Paper

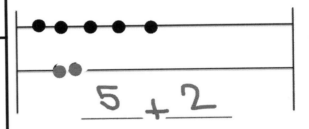

Abstract:
Show 4 ways to make 7

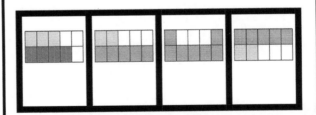

Math Processes/Practices
- Focus on reasoning
- Communicating thinking
- Modeling the Math
- Using Tools
- Thinking about pattern
- Looking for and making use of structure

Figure 7.32 Differentiation

Three Differentiated Lessons

In this series of lessons, students are working on the concept of composing and decomposing numbers using different types of models. They are developing this concept through concrete activities, pictorial activities and abstract activities. Here are some things to think about as you do these lessons.

Emergent	On Grade Level	Above Grade Level
Composing numbers within 4 and then 7.	Composing numbers within 10.	Composing higher numbers.

 Looking for Misunderstandings and Common Errors

There is actually a learning trajectory (Clements and Sarama, www.learningtrajectories. org) on composing and decomposing numbers. At kindergarten, students are working on composing numbers within 4 and then 7 and then 10 and then higher numbers. Students need to do this with many different models, including the ten frame, number bracelets, the rekenrek and number bonds.

Figure 7.33 Anchor Chart

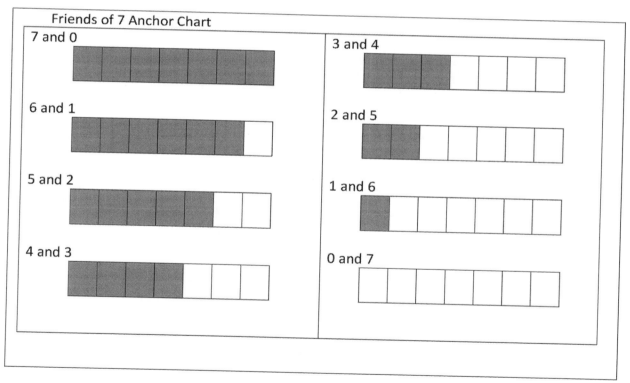

Figure 7.34 Concrete Introduction

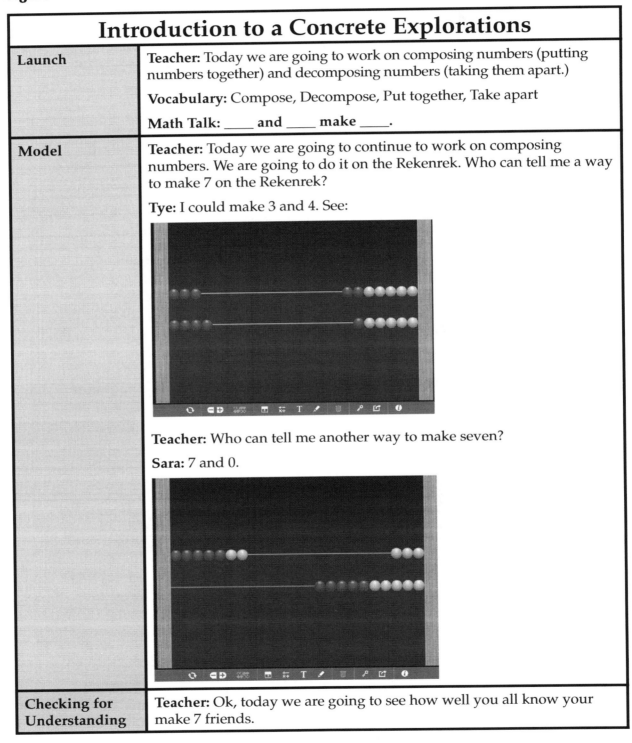

	Introduction to a Concrete Explorations
Launch	**Teacher:** Today we are going to work on composing numbers (putting numbers together) and decomposing numbers (taking them apart.) **Vocabulary:** Compose, Decompose, Put together, Take apart **Math Talk:** _____ and _____ make _____.
Model	**Teacher:** Today we are going to continue to work on composing numbers. We are going to do it on the Rekenrek. Who can tell me a way to make 7 on the Rekenrek? **Tye:** I could make 3 and 4. See: **Teacher:** Who can tell me another way to make seven? **Sara:** 7 and 0.
Checking for Understanding	**Teacher:** Ok, today we are going to see how well you all know your make 7 friends.

Figure 7.35 Student Activity

	Concrete Student Activity
Guided Practice/ Checking for Understanding	Students take turns showing different ways to make 7 on the rekenrek. Then, the teacher gives them a deck of cards and they practice composing the different numbers on the rekenrek. As they work independently, the teacher watches, asks them questions and takes notes. **Teacher:** Marta, tell me what you just did? **Marta:** I built 8. I did 4 and 4. **Teacher:** Is there another way to do 8? **Marta:** Yes, like 8 and 0.
Set up for Independent Practice	Teacher gives the students some time to work and then asks them what they have been working on. She wants to make sure that they understand the math they are doing and also to address any questions that students might have. They finish by wrapping up and going to workstations.

Figure 7.36 Lesson Close

Close
♦ What did we do today? ♦ What was the math we were practicing? ♦ Was this easy or tricky? ♦ Turn to a partner and state one thing you learned today.

Figure 7.37 Playing Cards

1	2	3	4	5
6	7	8	9	10

1	2	3	4	5
6	7	8	9	10

1	2	3	4	5
6	7	8	9	10

Visual Introduction

Figure 7.38 Visual Introduction

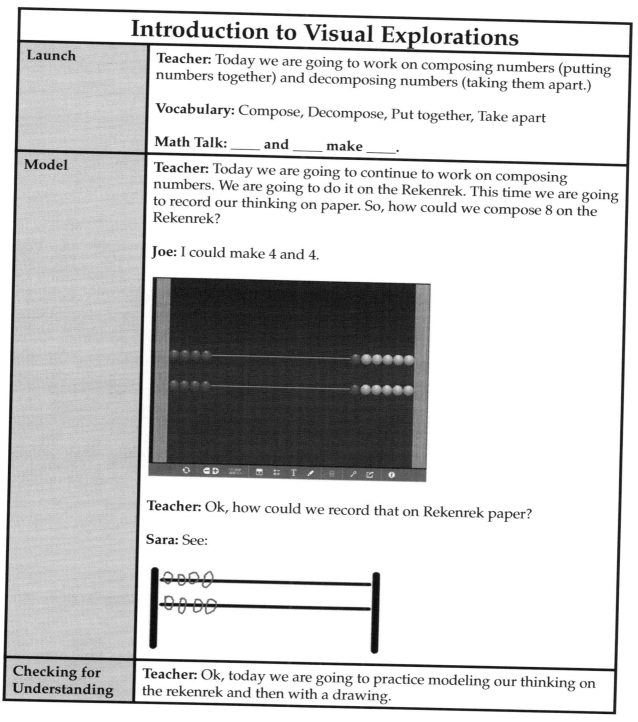

<table>
<tr><td colspan="2" align="center"><h2>Introduction to Visual Explorations</h2></td></tr>
<tr><td>Launch</td><td>Teacher: Today we are going to work on composing numbers (putting numbers together) and decomposing numbers (taking them apart.)

Vocabulary: Compose, Decompose, Put together, Take apart

Math Talk: ____ and ____ make ____.</td></tr>
<tr><td>Model</td><td>Teacher: Today we are going to continue to work on composing numbers. We are going to do it on the Rekenrek. This time we are going to record our thinking on paper. So, how could we compose 8 on the Rekenrek?

Joe: I could make 4 and 4.

Teacher: Ok, how could we record that on Rekenrek paper?

Sara: See:</td></tr>
<tr><td>Checking for Understanding</td><td>Teacher: Ok, today we are going to practice modeling our thinking on the rekenrek and then with a drawing.</td></tr>
</table>

Figure 7.39 Student Activity

Visual Student Activity

Guided Practice/ Checking for Understanding	Students take turns showing different ways to make numbers on the Rekenrek. Then, the teacher gives them a deck of cards and they practice composing the different numbers on the Rekenrek. They pull a number, make it and then record their work. As they work independently, the teacher watches, asks them questions and takes notes. **Teacher:** Tom tell me what you just did? **Marta:** I built 9. I did 4 and 5. 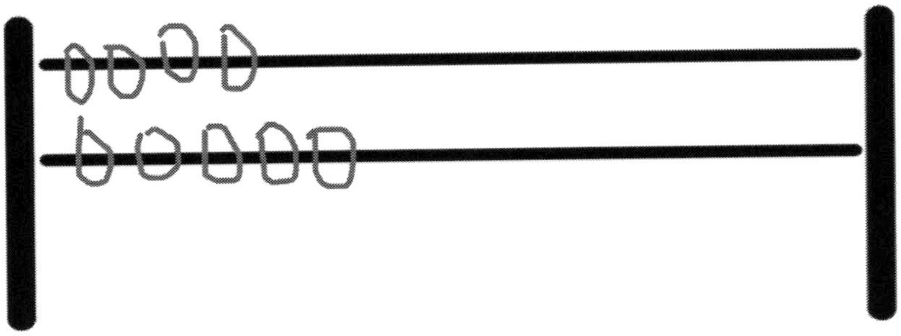 **Teacher:** Is there another way to do 9. **Marta:** Yes, like 9 and 0.
Set up for Independent Practice	Teacher gives the students some time to work and then asks them what they have been working on. She wants to make sure that they understand the math they are doing and also to address any questions that students might have. They finish by wrapping up and going to workstations.

Figure 7.40 Lesson Close

Close
◆ What did we do today?   ◆ What was the math we were practicing?   ◆ Was this easy or tricky?   ◆ Turn to a partner and state one thing you learned today.

Figure 7.41 Recording Sheet

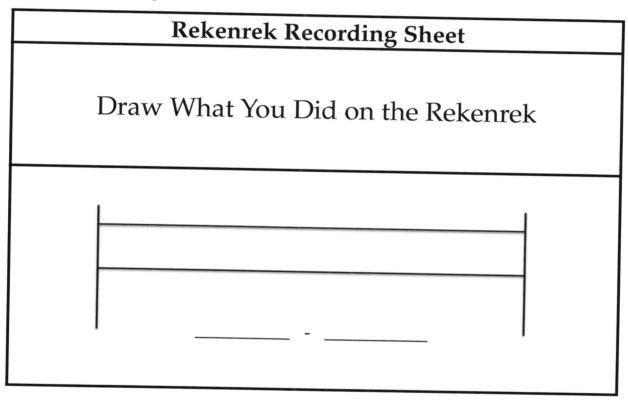

Rekenrek Recording Sheet

Draw What You Did on the Rekenrek

Abstract Introduction

Figure 7.42 Abstract Introduction

	Introduction Abstract Explorations
Launch	**Teacher:** Today we are going to work on putting together numbers and taking them apart. **Vocabulary:** Compose, Decompose, Put together, Take apart **Math Talk:** _____ and _____ make _____.
Model	**Teacher:** Today we are going to continue to work on making 7. We are going to play a card game today though. Let's look at our make 7 poster. What does this chart help us to see? 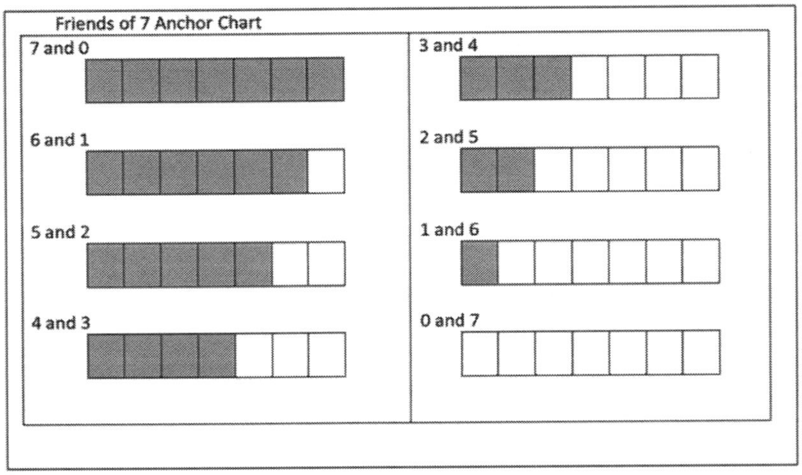 Friends of 7 Anchor Chart 7 and 0 3 and 4 6 and 1 2 and 5 5 and 2 1 and 6 4 and 3 0 and 7 **Student:** We can see the different ways to make 7. Like 0 and 7. **Teacher:** Who can tell me another way to make seven? **Student:** 7 and 0.
Checking for Understanding	**Teacher:** Ok, today we are going to see how well you all know how to compose (build) numbers.

Figure 7.43 Visual/Abstract Student Activity

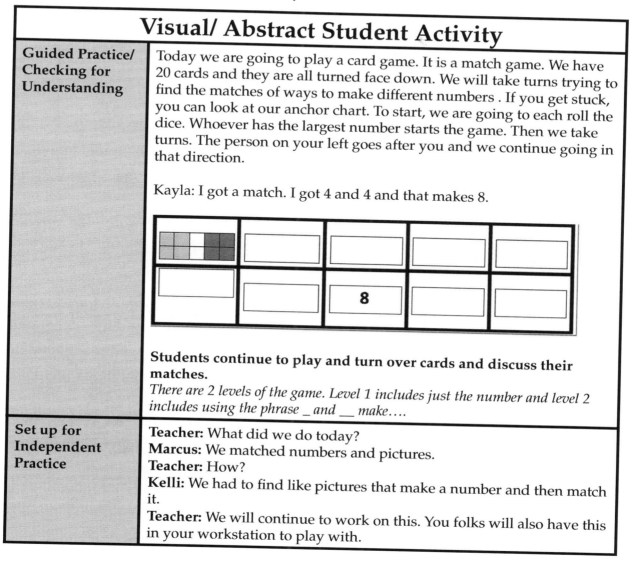

	Visual/ Abstract Student Activity
Guided Practice/ Checking for Understanding	Today we are going to play a card game. It is a match game. We have 20 cards and they are all turned face down. We will take turns trying to find the matches of ways to make different numbers . If you get stuck, you can look at our anchor chart. To start, we are going to each roll the dice. Whoever has the largest number starts the game. Then we take turns. The person on your left goes after you and we continue going in that direction. Kayla: I got a match. I got 4 and 4 and that makes 8. **Students continue to play and turn over cards and discuss their matches.** *There are 2 levels of the game. Level 1 includes just the number and level 2 includes using the phrase _ and __ make….*
Set up for Independent Practice	**Teacher:** What did we do today? **Marcus:** We matched numbers and pictures. **Teacher:** How? **Kelli:** We had to find like pictures that make a number and then match it. **Teacher:** We will continue to work on this. You folks will also have this in your workstation to play with.

Figure 7.44 Lesson Close

Close
♦ What did we do today? ♦ What was the math we were practicing? ♦ Was this easy or tricky? ♦ Turn to a partner and state one thing you learned today.

Figure 7.45 Math Game Cards Set

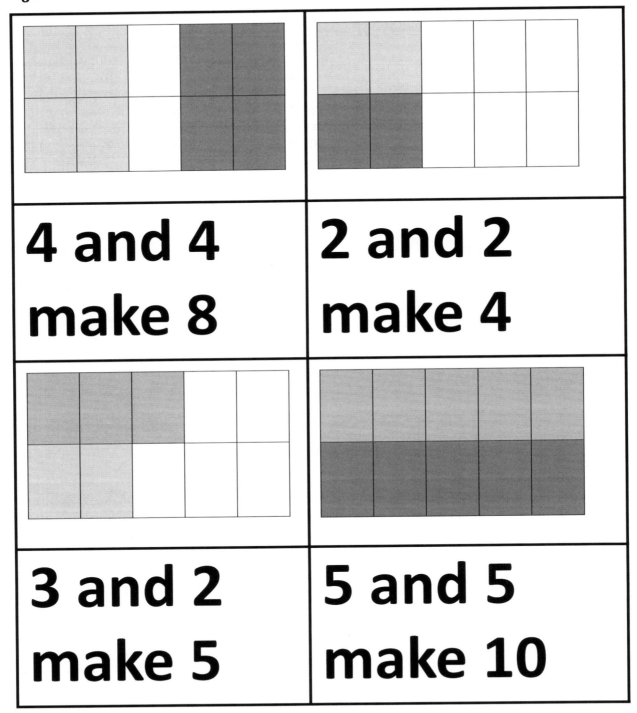

4 and 4 make 8

2 and 2 make 4

3 and 2 make 5

5 and 5 make 10

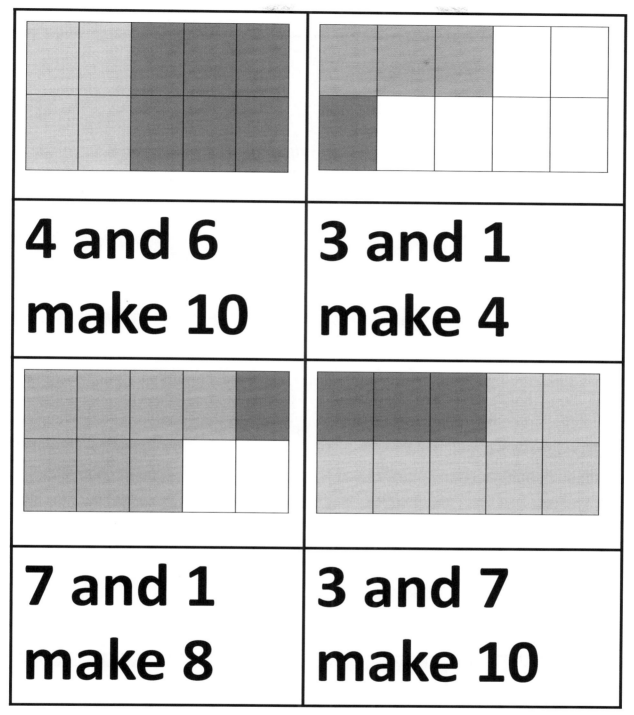

4 and 6 make 10

3 and 1 make 4

7 and 1 make 8

3 and 7 make 10

(Continued)

Figure 7.45 (Continued)

5	4
3	2
7	6
9	8
10	

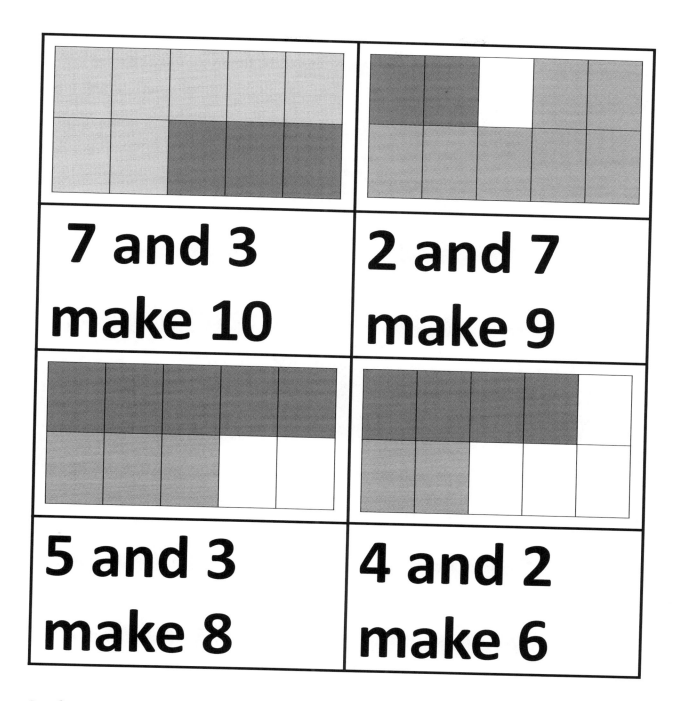

Section Summary

Composing and decomposing numbers is an essential skill. We need students to know different number combinations. The way that they get really strong with composing and decomposing numbers is to actually do it in a lot of different ways. This is why you should model this on so many different tools, including the rekenrek, ten frames, number bonds and different counters (especially cubes because you can make them into wands). Look up the Queen of Ten Math because she has some great routines around the ten wand.

Comparing Numbers

Overview

Figure 7.46 Overview

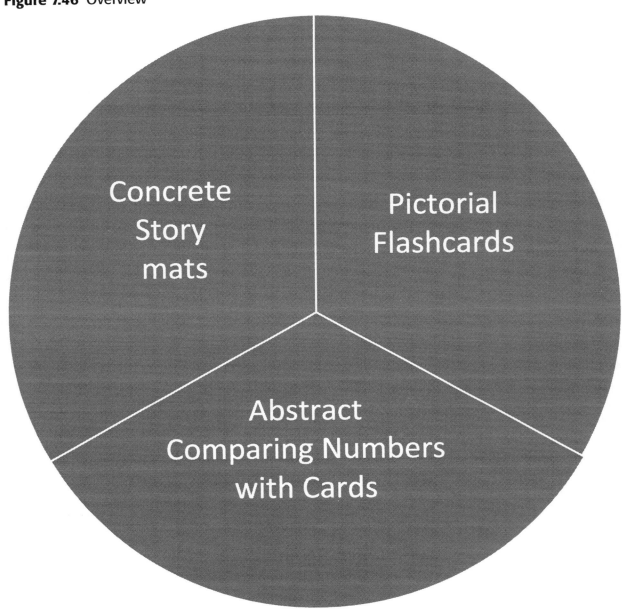

Figure 7.47 Planning Template

Comparing Numbers

Big Idea: Numbers can be compared.

Enduring Understanding: Students will understand and be able to compare numbers within 10.

Essential Question: What are the ways to compare numbers?

I can statement: I can compare numbers within 10.

Materials
♦ Tools: Cubes
♦ Templates: Ten Frame
♦ Cards
♦ Crayons

Questions
♦ What did we do today?
♦ What was the math we were practicing?
♦ Was this easy or tricky?
♦ Are there any questions?

Vocabulary & Language Frames

Compare, Match, Count

_____ is more than _____.

_____ is less than _____.

_____ is the same as _____.

Cycle of Engagement

Concrete: See it and build it

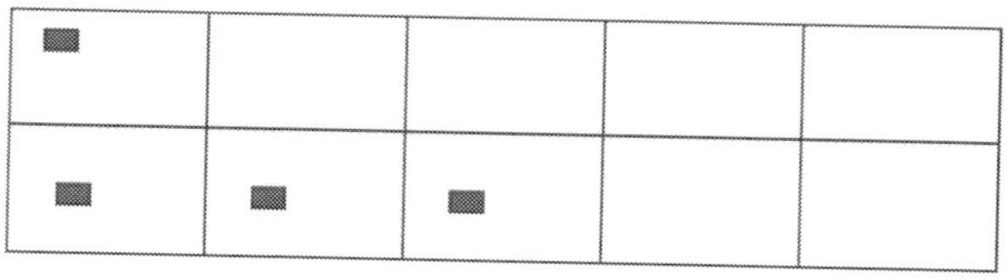

Pictorial: See it and draw it

Abstract: Compare Different Amounts
Which is larger? **9** or **2**

Math Processes/Practices
♦ Focus on reasoning
♦ Communicating thinking
♦ Modeling the Math
♦ Using Tools
♦ Thinking about pattern
♦ Looking for and making use of structure

Figure 7.48 Differentiation

Three Differentiated Lessons
In this series of lessons, students are working on the concept of comparing numbers using different types of models. They are developing this concept through concrete activities, pictorial activities and abstract activities. Here are some things to think about as you do these lessons.

Emergent	On Grade Level	Above Grade Level
Review quantities. Compare numbers within 5.	Use different models to compare numbers within 10.	Expand the number range.

 Looking for Misunderstandings and Common Errors

There are so many levels of teaching students to compare. See the learning trajectories by Clements and Sarama (www.learningtrajectories.org). Students have to learn to compare first by actually matching and then by counting and then by comparing written numbers. They should be able to identify whether the number of objects in one group is greater than, less than or equal to the number of objects in another group.

Figure 7.49 Anchor Chart: Comparing Numbers

Cycle of Engagement

Concrete: Comparing in the 10 frame with counters

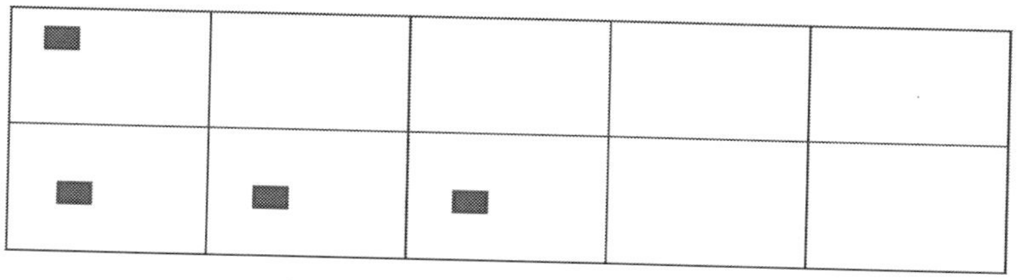

▪				
▪	▪	▪		

Pictorial: Comparing by drawing

Abstract: Comparing Numbers
Which is larger? **4** or **1**

Concrete Lesson

Figure 7.50 Concrete Introduction

Introduction
Concrete Explorations

Launch	**Teacher:** Today we are going to work on ways to compare numbers. **Vocabulary:** compare, less than, more, same as **Math Talk:** I have more than _____. I have less than _____. I have the same amount as _____.
Model	**Teacher:** Today we are going to compare numbers by matching. You and your partner are going to each pull a number. You will each use a different color circle to represent your number. You will match them up in a twenty frame and compare the amounts. Whoever has more gets a cube. Whoever gets 10 cubes first wins. Who wants to go first? **Timmy:** I will go. I pulled a 5. **Rachel:** I pulled a 7. I have more. I have 2 more than he does. 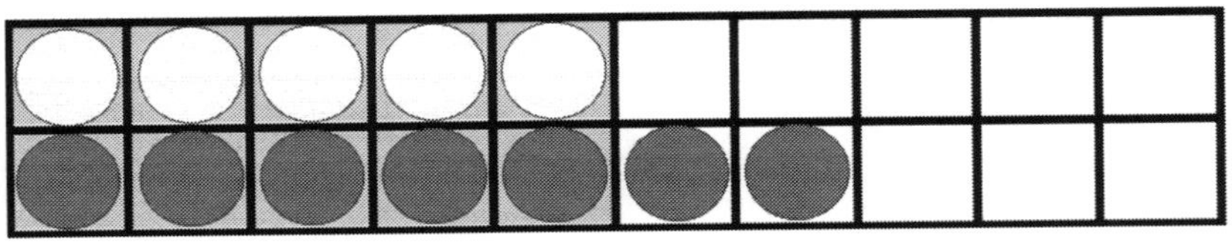
Checking for Understanding	**Teacher:** Let's do it again? **Terri:** I will go. I pulled a 5. **Roy:** I pulled a 9. I have more. I have 4 more than she does. 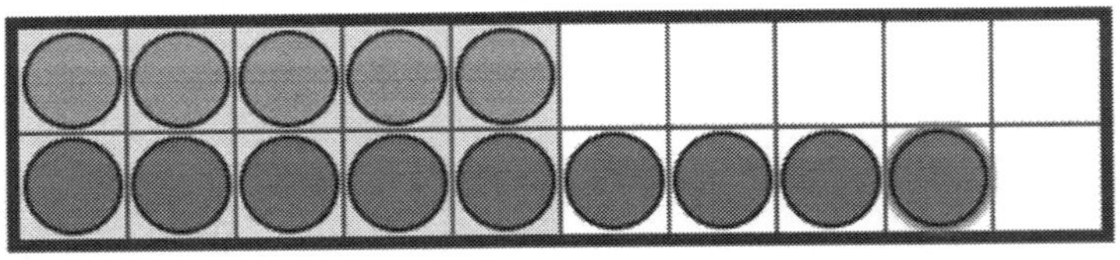 **Teacher:** Ok, we are going to play this with partners.

Figure 7.51 Student Activity

Student Concrete Activity

Guided Practice/ Checking for Understanding	The teacher watches the students play the compare game. The teacher watches, takes notes, asks questions and scaffolds with prompts and cues as needed. **Hong:** I pulled a 7. **Nancy:** I pulled a 7. We have the same amount. **Hong:** It's equal. We both get a point! 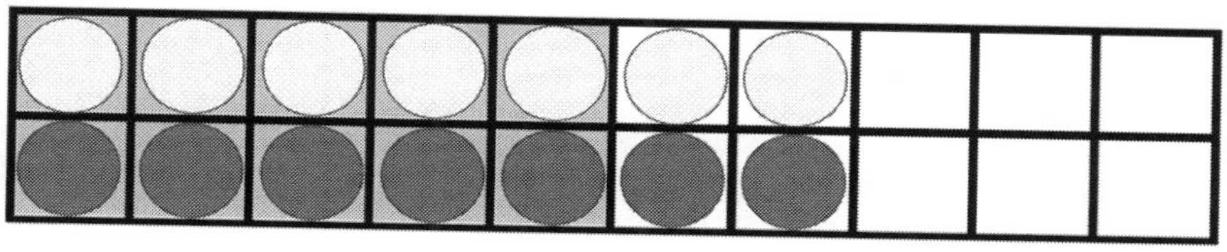
Set up for Independent Practice	After students play for a while, the teacher brings everybody back together and facilitates a discussion about comparing numbers. The teacher asks students what is easy and what is tricky. The teacher also asks the students to explain what it means to compare numbers and how to do it.

Figure 7.52 Lesson Close

Close

- What did we do today?
- What was the math we were practicing?
- Was this easy or tricky?
- Turn to a partner and state one thing you learned today.

Figure 7.53 Visual Introduction

Introduction
Visual Explorations

Launch	**Teacher:** Today we are going to work on ways to compare numbers. **Vocabulary:** compare, fewer, less more, same as **Math Talk:** I have more. I have less. I have the same amount.
Model	**Teacher:** Today we are going to compare numbers by counting. You and your partner are going to each pull a number. You will use your number path to decide who has the largest number. So each person will put a different marker on the number path to compare the numbers. **Tania:** I will go. I pulled a 4. **Roy:** I pulled a 10. I have more. I win a point. 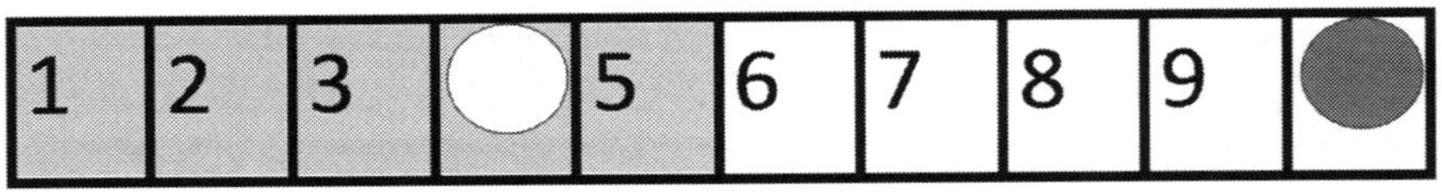 | 1	2	3	◯	5	6	7	8	9	⬤	
Checking for Understanding	**Teacher:** Ok, I am going to give each partner a game pack and you are going to play and I am going to watch you and talk with you as you do it.

Figure 7.54 Student Activity

	Student Visual Activity
Guided Practice/ Checking for Understanding	The teacher watches the students play the compare game. The teacher watches, takes notes, asks questions and scaffolds with prompts and cues as needed. **Yesenia:** I pulled a 3. **Miguel:** I pulled a 9. I have more. 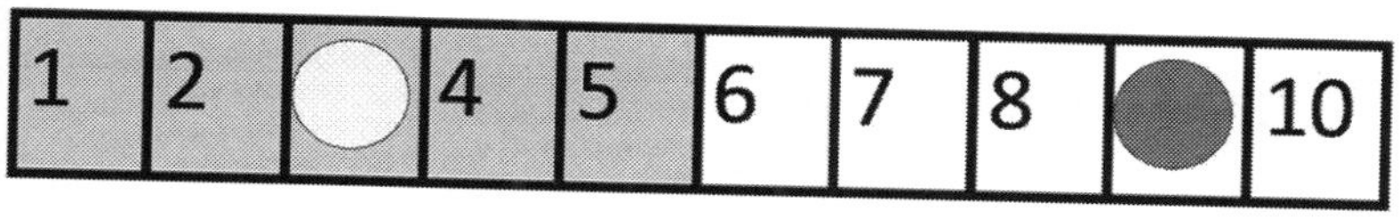 `1  2  ○  4  5  6  7  8  ●  10` **Teacher:** Miguel how do you know that you have more? **Miguel:** Because it is way over here. It is more than 3. **Teacher:** Yesenia, if he has more, then you have what? **Yesenia:** I don't have as many. **Teacher:** Yes, Yesenia, you have fewer than he does.
Set up for Independent Practice	After students play for a while, the teacher brings everybody back together and facilitates a discussion about comparing numbers. The teacher asks students what is easy and what is tricky. The teacher also asks the students to explain what it means to compare numbers and how to do it.

Figure 7.55 Lesson Close

Close
♦ What did we do today? ♦ What was the math we were practicing? ♦ Was this easy or tricky? ♦ Turn to a partner and state one thing you learned today.

Abstract Lesson

Figure 7.56 Abstract Introduction

Introduction
Abstract Explorations

Launch	**Teacher:** Today we are going to work on ways to compare numbers. **Vocabulary:** compare, fewer, more, same as **Math Talk:** I have more. I have fewer. I have the same amount.
Model	**Teacher:** Today we are going to compare numbers by using our mental number line. You and your partner are going to each pull a number. You will just compare your numbers. If you need to, you can use your tools to help you figure out the answer, but try it first and then check if you need to. **Jason:** I will go. I pulled a 3 **David:** I pulled a 7. I have more. $$\boxed{7} \quad \boxed{3}$$ **Teacher:** How do you know? **David:** Because 7 comes after 3 when you are counting. **Jason:** Are you sure? **David:** Yes, I can prove it by counting…1,2,3,4,5,6,7
Checking for Understanding	**Teacher:** Ok, we are going to continue doing this. Remember you can count and also look at your number line.

Figure 7.57 Student Activity

Student Abstract Activity	
Guided Practice/ Checking for Understanding	The teacher watches the students play the compare game. The teacher watches, takes notes, asks questions and scaffolds with prompts and cues as needed. **Harry:** I pulled a 2. **Grace:** I pulled a 10. I have more! I win a point! ### 2 10 **Teacher:** Grace how do you know that you have more? **Grace:** Because 10 is more than 2. I can prove it. See: 10 (she shows It on her fingers and then compare it to 2 which she also shows on her fingers).
Set up for Independent Practice	After students play for a while, the teacher brings everybody back together and facilitates a discussion about comparing numbers. The teacher asks students what is easy and what is tricky. The teacher also asks the students to explain what it means to compare numbers and how to do it.

Figure 7.58 Lesson Close

Close
◆ What did we do today? ◆ What was the math we were practicing? ◆ Was this easy or tricky? ◆ Turn to a partner and state one thing you learned today.

Section Summary

Comparing numbers is so important. There are so many different types of comparing. Students have to learn to compare, items of different sizes and items of the same sizes. There is also a trajectory for learning to compare numbers. They need to start with matching amounts and then comparing by counting using a number line and then eventually being able to do it with written numbers just referring to their mental number line in their head. This scaffolds student understanding into the concept of comparing. It is important not to skip any of these steps, so students have a strong foundation for comparing numbers.

Depth of Knowledge

Depth of Knowledge is a framework that encourages us to ask questions that require that students think, reason, explain, defend and justify their thinking (Webb, 2002). Here is a snapshot of what that can look like in terms of place value work. It is important to continually reflect on what the level of the lesson is. In working in small groups on problem solving, be sure to ask open questions so that students can think and reason out loud with others.

Figure 7.59 DOK Chart

	What are different strategies and models that we can use to explore counting by 10's?	What are different strategies and models to explore subitizing?	What are different strategies and models that we can use to compose and decompose numbers?	What are different strategies and models that we can use to compare numbers?
DOK Level 1 (These are questions where students are required to simply recall/reproduce an answer/do a procedure.)	Count by 10's to 100	How many do you see? (subitizing within 4 and 5)	What are some ways to make 7?	Which is more 5 or 3?
DOK Level 2 (These are questions where students have to use information, think about concepts and reason.) This is considered a more challenging problem than a level 1 problem.	What does it mean to count by 10's? What are we doing when we count by 10's?	What do you see? How do you see it? (subitizing up to 7)	Circle all the ways you see to make 10. 5 + 5 4 + 4 3 + 7 2 + 8 1 + 8 1 + 9 10 + 0	Tell me a number that is more than 7. Tell me a number less than 5.
DOK Level 3 (These are questions where students have to reason, plan, explain, justify and defend their thinking.)	Show me two different ways to model counting by 10's. Explain your thinking.	Look at these cards and pick out three different ways that show 10. (subitizing up to 10)	I am going to give you a number and you tell me how many more to 10: 2 8 9 5	Explain what it means to compare numbers. What does before/after/in between mean? Give me an example. Tell me a number that comes before/after/in between another number. Prove you are correct. Model it in two different ways. Explain how you know your answer is correct.

Figure 7.60 Asking Rigorous Questions

DOK 1	DOK 2 **At this level students explain their thinking.**	DOK 3 **At this level students have to justify, defend and prove their thinking with objects, drawings and diagrams.**
What is the answer to ??? Can you model the problem? Can you identify the answer that matches this equation?	How do you know that the equation is correct? Can you pick the correct answer and explain why it is correct? How can you model that problem in more than one way? What is another way to model that problem? Can you model that on the . . . ??? Give me an example of a . . . type of problem. Which answer is incorrect? Explain your thinking.	Can you prove that your answer is correct? Prove that . . . Explain why that is the answer. Show me how to solve that and explain what you are doing.

Resources

A great resource for asking open questions is Marion Small's *Good Questions: Great ways to differentiate mathematics instruction in the standards-based classroom* (2017). Also, Robert Kaplinsky has done a great job in pushing our thinking forward with the Depth of Knowledge Matrices he created (https://robertkaplinsky.com/depth-knowledge-matrix-elementary-math/). Kentucky Department of Education (2007) also has great DOK math matrices.

Key Points

♦ Counting
♦ Subitizing
♦ Composing
♦ Comparing

Chapter Summary

Counting and cardinality is such an important aspect of kindergarten. Many of these concepts lay the foundation for the rest of the work that students will do throughout their schooling. We know that counting is essential. We understand that subitizing is a bedrock of arithmetic. We know that allowing students to compose and decompose numbers throughout the year builds flexibility. We want students to be able to compare numbers and have the language to talk about what they are doing. Throughout the year, students should be encouraged to work on the language and work with tools to build a strong sense of number. We have to consider where students are along the learning trajectories to know how to design the lessons based on student need.

Reflection Questions

1. In what ways are you working on counting and cardinality through the cycle of engagement with your students?
2. Are you making sure that students have ample opportunities to practice subitizing throughout the year?
3. How are you providing opportunities for students to become competent with composing and decomposing activities throughout the year?
4. Are you making sure that students have an opportunity to compare by matching activities, counting activities and then using their mental number lines?
5. What are your big "Aha" moments in this unit? What do you need to rethink?

References

Baroody, A. (1987). *Children's Mathematical Thinking*. New York: Teachers College Press.

Clements, D. (1999). *Subitizing: What Is It? Why Teach It? Teaching Children Mathematics*. Reston, VA: NCTM.

Clements, D. (2019). Retrieved from www.learningtrajectories.org/

Desoete, A., Ceulemans, A., Roeyers, H., & Huylebroeck, A. (2009). Subitizing or Counting as Possible Screening Variables for Learning Disabilities in Mathematics Education or Learning? *Educational Research Review*, 4, 55–66.

Geary, D. C., van Marle, K., Chu, F. W., Rouder, J., Hoard, M. K., & Nugent, L. (2017). Early Conceptual Understanding of Cardinality Predicts Superior School-entry Number-system Knowledge. *Psychological Science*, 29(2), 191–205.

Jordan, N. C., Kaplan, D., Ramineni, C., & Locuniak, M. N. (2008). Development of Number Combination Skill in the Early School Years: When do Fingers Help? *Developmental Science*, 11(5), 662–668.

Jordan, N. C., Kaplan, D., Ramineni, C., & Locuniak, M. N. (2009). Early Math Matters: Kindergarten Number Competence and Later Mathematics Outcomes. *Developmental Psychology*, 3(45), 850–867.

Kentucky Department of Education. (2007). *Support Materials for Core Content for Assessment Version 4.1 Mathematics*. Retrieved January 15, 2017 from the internet.

Locuniak, M. N., & Jordan, N. C. (2008). Using Kindergarten Number Sense to Predict Calculation Fluency in Second Grade. *Journal of Learning Disabilities*, 41(5), 451–459.

Ma, L. (1999). *Knowing and Teaching Elementary Mathematics: Teachers' Understanding of Fundamental Mathematics in China and the United States*. Mahwah, NJ: Lawrence Erlbaum Associates Inc.

Nguyen, T., Watts, T. W., Duncan, G. J., Clements, D. H., Sarama, J., Wolfe, C. B., & Spitler, M. E. (2016). Which Preschool Mathematics Competencies Are Most Predictive of Fifth Grade Achievement? *Early Childhood Research Quarterly*, 36, 550–560. https://doi.org/10.1016/j.ecresq.2016.02.003

Richardson, K. (1997). *Math Time: The Learning Environment*. K. Antell (Ed.). Wilmington, DE: Educational Enrichment.

Small, M. (2017). *Good Questions: Great Ways to Differentiate Math in the Standards Based Classroom*. New York: Teachers College Press.

Webb, N. (2002). An Analysis of the Alignment Between Mathematics Standards and Assessments for Three States. Paper presented at *the Annual Meeting of the American Educational Research Association*. New Orleans, LA.

8

Place Value

Place value is a very important concept in kindergarten. Researchers note that it should be taught throughout the elementary grades through a continuing spiral of complexity (National Council of Teachers of Mathematics, 2000; National Research Council, 2009). It is considered a foundational skill for more complex mathematics in upper grades. Kindergarten is where the concept of tens and ones are introduced through 20. The other place value concepts are incorporated into counting and cardinality standards but are the foundation to place value in the other grades, such as verbally counting through 100 from any number, counting by 10's, counting out 20 objects and comparing numbers.

The National Research Council (NRC, 2009) states that "to begin to understand the base-ten place value system, children must be able to view ten ones as forming a single unit of ten" (p. 45). This concept means that students should be able to "unitize" (Fosnot & Dolk, 2001). The idea is a unit of ten is a benchmark number in children's mathematical development (Van de Walle, 2003).

Because there is so much emphasis on counting by ones in kindergarten, when students are introduced to the concept of a group of ten and ones it can be confusing. So, when you ask them to tell you about 16 they will say things like I see, 1 and 6. They get confused between the number and the groups of ten and ones. They are just naming the numbers they see without understanding the position and the value of that position. Our goal in kindergarten is to get them to understand the idea of a group of ten and some extra ones. This is a big idea for little ones to conceive. So, we have to take our time and reinforce it throughout the spring.

The idea of understanding a group of ten and some ones must be explored in many different ways through a cycle of engagement of concrete, pictorial and abstract representations. This approach has received the Access Center Research Continuum's highest ranking of "evidence-based research" (Access Center, 2004). Researchers talk about the need for students to learn and own place value by building groups of tens with bean sticks first so they can build a stick of 10 and see the loose ones. They should also build them with cubes that they can stick together to make a group of ten and have some extra ones. They should explore this concept on the ten frame as well.

Remember that students have to own the model and make meaning of it. It shouldn't be that the model is imposed as an understanding of the concept. They have to have plenty of opportunities to construct their understanding by building tens and ones. These are called groupable models. Students need to be able to see and discuss the relationship of the tens and ones and how a group of ten becomes a ten. They need to practice grouping the singles into a ten, so that they can see when they have ten singles they can group them as one group of ten. These can be called "put together/take apart" models.

Only after students thoroughly understand this concept of a group of ten and some extra ones should they be introduced to place value blocks—which is considered a premade economy. These are considered to be pregrouped models. Students cannot take them apart or put

DOI: 10.4324/9781003169529-8

them together. The 10 single pieces are grouped and then exchanged or traded for a ten. I also would eventually introduce some place value disks as well. Research notes that the more scaffolding opportunities that are used, the better (McGuire & Kinzie, 2013). Students should "use multiple models to develop initial understandings of place value and the base-ten number system" (NCTM, 2000).

It is very important that students can talk about place value and connect those words to ideas. They need several opportunities to be able to represent numbers in a variety of ways. They should be exploring things concretely, pictorially and abstractly. They should be able to express the numbers for example as 16 but also as 1 ten and 6 ones. There is a cycle of engagement of counting by 1's, counting by groups and singles and then counting by 10's and 1's. This concept was introduced and built really well in a program called *Math Their Way*. In this game, students explore different bases through a game called "Zurkle" where students would have to group items depending on what the "Zurkle" number was. Eventually the students worked up to "Zurkle" being groups of tens and ones. Eventually, the main focus is the idea that "10 is a special number in math" (McGuire & Kinzie, 2013). We have to spend a great deal of time developing this foundational concept and give students plenty of opportunities to make and count groups of 10.

The other big takeaway here is that understanding place value takes time. It is not a two-week unit. The idea that understanding grows over time (students have an emergent understanding) is described by Carpenter and Lehrer's (1999) "understanding is not an all-or-none phenomenon . . . virtually all complex ideas or processes can be understood at a number of levels and in quite different ways" (p. 20).)

Place value concepts can be introduced in two weeks perhaps, but from then on the idea should be reinforced throughout the rest of the weeks of school year through energizers, routines and workstations. Once place value is introduced, there should be a place value workstation where students can work with the concepts throughout the rest of the year.

Figure 8.1 Place Value Triangle

The Place Value Triangle includes experiences of "Saying, writing and building" Numbers. There should be strong emphasis on representing place value in a variety of ways (Baker & Ward, 2015) . It is important that students are making the connections between the symbols, the verbal numeral names (spoken word) and concrete representations (Ginsberg, Greens, & Balfanz, 2003)

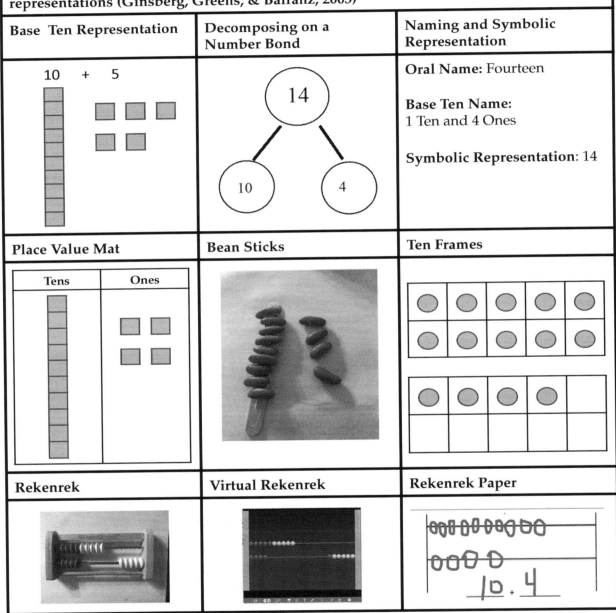

Base Ten Representation	Decomposing on a Number Bond	Naming and Symbolic Representation
10 + 5	14 / 10 / 4	**Oral Name:** Fourteen **Base Ten Name:** 1 Ten and 4 Ones **Symbolic Representation:** 14
Place Value Mat Tens / Ones	**Bean Sticks**	**Ten Frames**
Rekenrek	**Virtual Rekenrek**	**Rekenrek Paper**

Figure 8.2 Research Chart

Research on Prekindergartens and Place Value: Implications for K	Visual Place Value Chart
Research indicates that students "possess a conceptual understanding of the ones place prior to the tens place and initially struggle with the concept of unitizing groups of ten." Researchers have found that the math talk which teachers have with students and the "quality of the interactions" and activities need to be done in a way that "support children's thinking and learning"(McGuire & Kinzie, 2013).	Students work with ten frames and snap cubes. They get a physical visual chart of the number representations, a visual color coded chart that has both the numbers and the corresponding ten frame representations (red for tens place and green for the ones place), so that the students can "make the connections between the relative magnitude of numbers (quantitative value) to the written symbols (digits) that they represent as well as support children's ability to accept the different equivalences of numerical representations" (Ginsburg, Greenes, & Balfanz, 2003; Ainsworth, 1999 cited McGuire & Kinzie, 2013). Furthermore, the color-coded representations help the students to make the connections between the symbols, the spoken name and the representations. Students are encouraged to look at the patterns and predict what the new numbers will be in the chart. They make "predications about what number will come next and how many ten frames/leftovers each number will have" (McGuire & Kinzie, 2013).

Importance of Unitizing	Working With Individual Snap Cubes to Represent Tens and Ones by Making Exchanges	Scaffolding Practices and Questioning Strategies Affect Student Language Production
Fosnot and Dolk (2001) discuss the importance of unitizing for young learners. "Unitizing underlies the understanding of place value; ten objects becomes one ten. Unitizing requires that children use number to count not only objects but also groups—and to count them both simultaneously. The whole is thus seen as a group of a number of objects. The parts together become the new whole, and the parts (the objects in the group) and the whole (the group) can be considered simultaneously. For learners, this is a shift in perspective. Children have just learned to count ten objects, one by one. Unitizing these ten things as one thing—one group—requires almost negating their original idea of number" (p. 11).	Students used snap cubes to create groups of ten by connecting individual snap cubes. They compared their creations with the Visual Number Chart. The focus is "the exchange principle, e.g. ten ones is the same as one of ten and explore the concept of leftovers (McGuire & Kinzie, 2013)."	"It is very important for students to have the physical objects (concrete scaffolding) and the verbal scaffolding so that they can go beyond simple yes or no answers" McGuire & Kinzie (2013).

Figure 8.3 Visual Place Value Chart 1

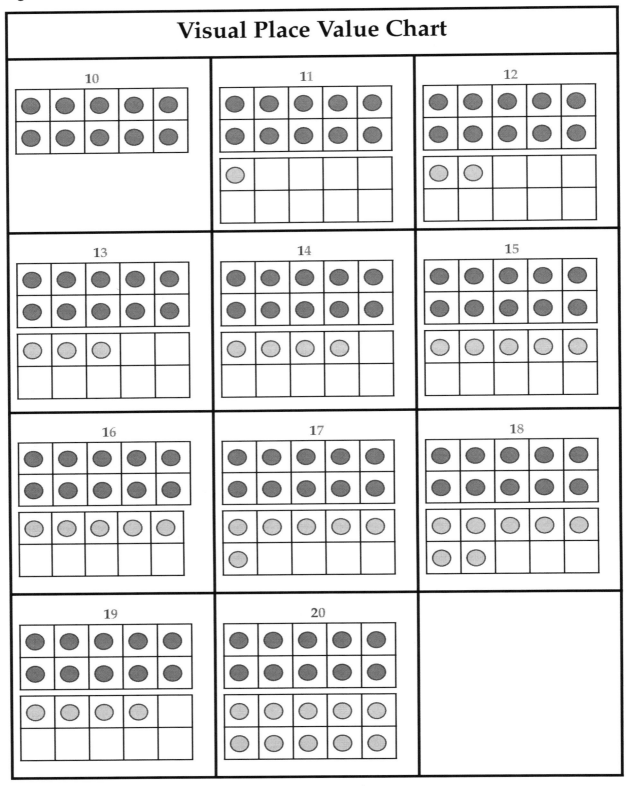

https://apps.mathlearningcenter.org/number-pieces/

Figure 8.4 Visual Place Value Chart 2

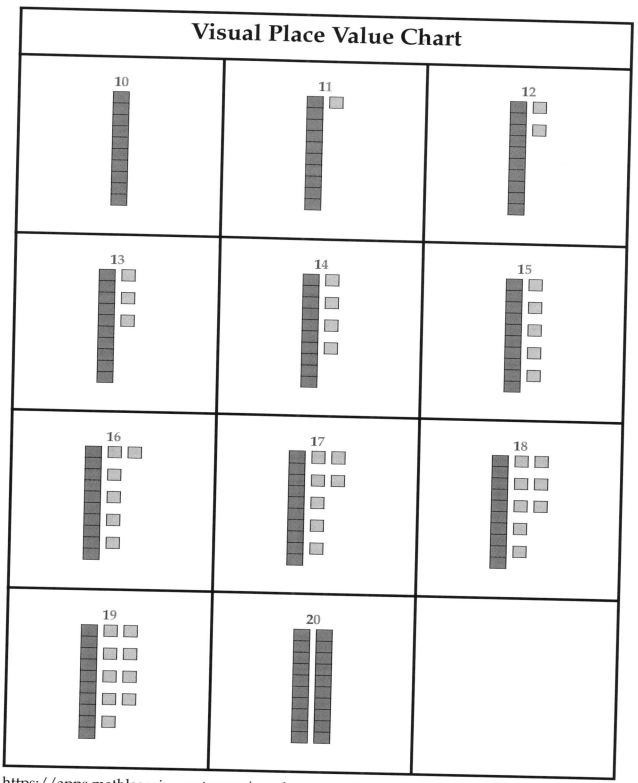

https://apps.mathlearningcenter.org/number-pieces/

In this chapter, we will explore:

- ◆ Exploring place value with ten frames
- ◆ Teen numbers on the rekenrek
- ◆ Working with place value blocks
- ◆ Comparing teen numbers

Exploring Place Value With Ten Frames

Overview

Figure 8.5 Overview

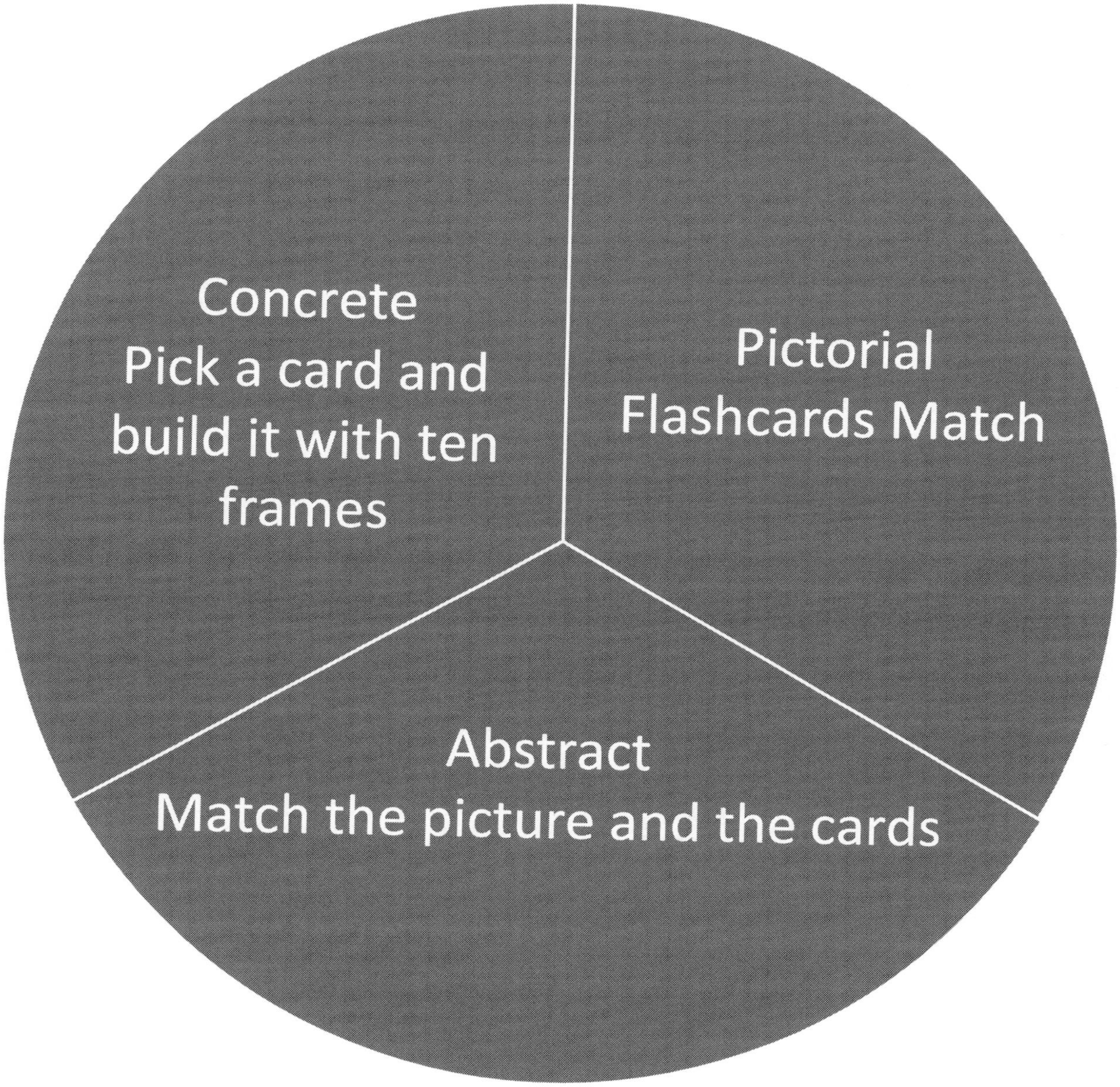

Concrete
Pick a card and
build it with ten
frames

Pictorial
Flashcards Match

Abstract
Match the picture and the cards

Figure 8.6 Planning Template

Exploring Place Value with Ten Frames

Big Idea: Tens and Ones

Enduring Understanding: A number can be 1 group of a ten and remainders

Essential Question: How can we represent teen numbers?

Content Question: What is a teen number? How can you break a teen number up into tens and ones?

I can statement:
I can recognize and name teen numbers.
I can build teen numbers.
I can draw teen numbers.

Materials
- Tools: Rekenrek
- Rekenrek Paper
- Templates: Ten Frame
- Cards
- Crayons

Questions
- What are the names of teen numbers?
- How can I break a teen number into tens and ones?
- What do the leftovers mean?

Cycle of Engagement
Concrete: Rekenrek

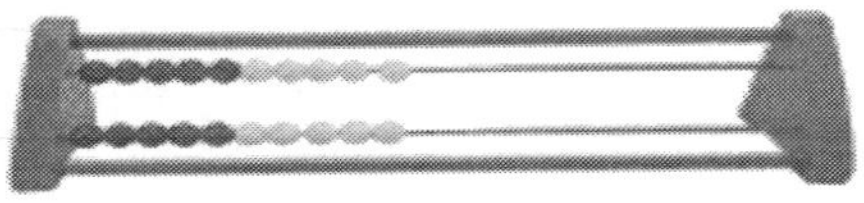

Pictorial:
Flashcards with numbers and pictures

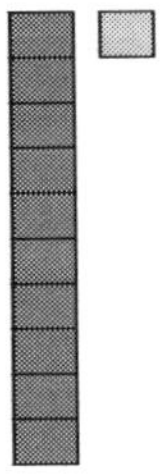

Abstract:
1 ten and 9 ones

Vocabulary & Language Frames

- Teen Number
- Model
- Ten
- Ones
- Leftovers

A 10 and ____ones make the number _____

Figure 8.7 Differentiation

Three Differentiated Lessons		
In this series of lessons, students are working on the concept of teen numbers using different types of models. They are developing this concept through concrete activities, pictorial activities and abstract activities. Here are some things to think about as you do these lessons.		
Emergent Level	**On Grade Level**	**Above Grade Level**
Exploring grouping ones into a ten and remainders (11,12,13)	Use different models to represent expressions and equations of all teen numbers.	Expand the number range.

 Looking for Misunderstandings and Common Errors

It is really important to work with groupable manipulatives where students can practice making tens and then counting the leftovers. They should have lots of opportunities to do this and then later on move to pregrouped items like the place value blocks.

Figure 8.8 Anchor Chart

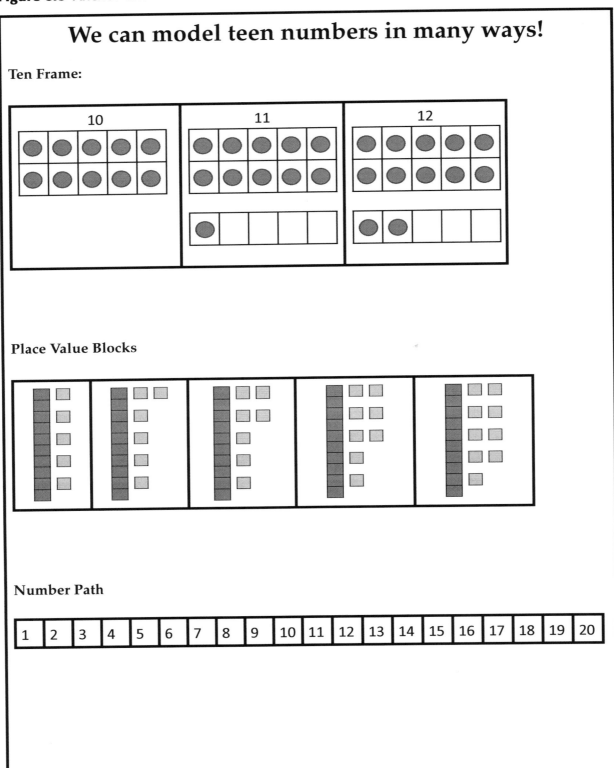

We can model teen numbers in many ways!

Ten Frame:

Place Value Blocks

Number Path

| 1 | 2 | 3 | 4 | 5 | 6 | 7 | 8 | 9 | 10 | 11 | 12 | 13 | 14 | 15 | 16 | 17 | 18 | 19 | 20 |

Concrete Lesson

Figure 8.9 Concrete Introduction

<table>
<tr>
<td colspan="2" align="center"><h2>Introduction to
Concrete Explorations</h2></td>
</tr>
<tr>
<td>Launch</td>
<td>

Teacher: Today we are going to work on exploring teen numbers with our twenty frames.

Vocabulary: model, teen number, tens, ones

Math Talk: _____ and ____ make _____. _____ + _____ = _____

</td>
</tr>
<tr>
<td>Model</td>
<td>

Teacher: Today we are going to work on making teen numbers. What is a teen number?

Jamal: It's like 14.

Teacher: Yes. Who can give me another example?

Tami: Like 16

</td>
</tr>
<tr>
<td>Checking for Understanding</td>
<td>

Teacher: Excellent examples. They have a ten and some leftovers, like we have been talking about on the rug. Today we are going to build some on our twenty frames. I am going to give you a mat so you can build a number that I show you. Here is the number: 11

Kelli: I know…. It is 10 and then 1 left over.

Teacher: Great!

Teacher: Ok, smarty pants…. I am going to give you another one. 15 (the students build it). Ok, now I am going to give each one of you a number to build and then let you go around and say your number and explain how you built it.

</td>
</tr>
</table>

Figure 8.10 Student Activity

	Concrete Student Activity
Guided Practice/ Checking for Understanding	The teacher passes out the twenty frame mats. You will build your number and then explain to the group your thinking. **Todd:** I had 15. I made 10 and then 5 leftovers. 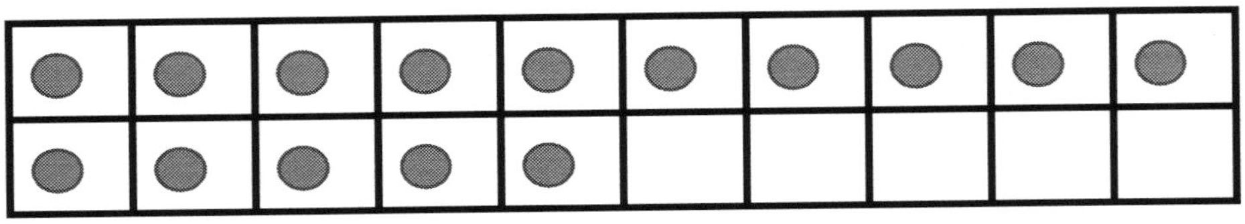 **Teacher:** So what makes 15? **Melissa:** 10 and 5. **All the students get a chance to share their thinking.**
Set up for Independent Practice	*The teacher asks the students questions individually. Then, the teacher goes around the circle and has each student share one of their problems and explain what they did. At the end, the teacher asks students to talk about the math, and if it is easy or tricky.*

Figure 8.11 Lesson Close

Close
♦ What did we do today?
♦ What was the math we were practicing?
♦ What were we doing with the count on strategy?
♦ Was this easy or tricky?
♦ Turn to a partner and state one thing you learned today.

Figure 8.12 Twenty Frame Template Visual Lesson

Figure 8.13 Number Cards

11	12	13	14	15
10	19	18	17	16

Figure 8.14 Visual Introduction

Introduction to Visual Representations

Launch	**Teacher:** Today we are going to work on place value.
	Vocabulary: model, tens, ones, teen number
	Math Talk: _____ and ____ make _____. _____ + _____ = _____
Model	**Teacher:** Today we are going to pick a number and draw it on our double ten frame. See this is my card.

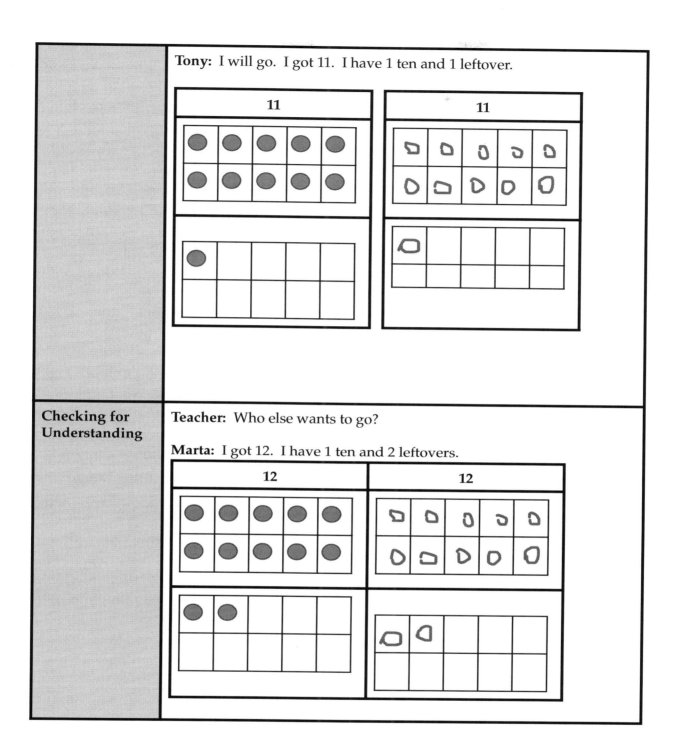

Tony: I will go. I got 11. I have 1 ten and 1 leftover.

11	11

Checking for Understanding

Teacher: Who else wants to go?

Marta: I got 12. I have 1 ten and 2 leftovers.

12	12

Figure 8.15 Student Activity

Visual Student Activity

Guided Practice/ Checking for Understanding	**Teacher:** Who else wants to go? **Marta:** I got 16. I have 1 ten and 6 leftovers. 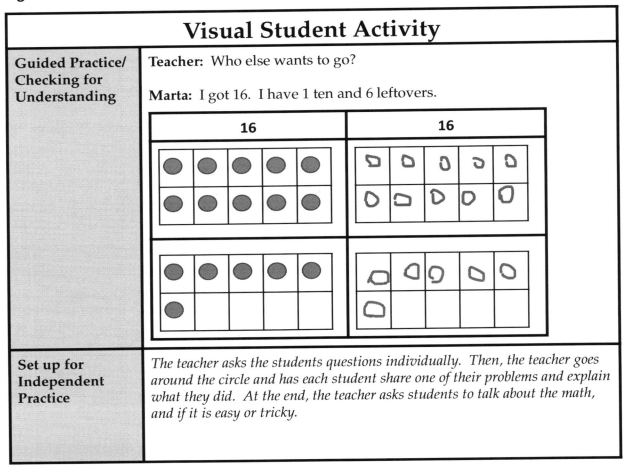
Set up for Independent Practice	*The teacher asks the students questions individually. Then, the teacher goes around the circle and has each student share one of their problems and explain what they did. At the end, the teacher asks students to talk about the math, and if it is easy or tricky.*

Figure 8.16 Lesson Close

Close

♦ What did we do today?
♦ What was the math we were practicing?
♦ Was this easy or tricky?
♦ Turn to a partner and state one thing you learned today.

Figure 8.17 Ten Frame Cards

Pull and Draw it!

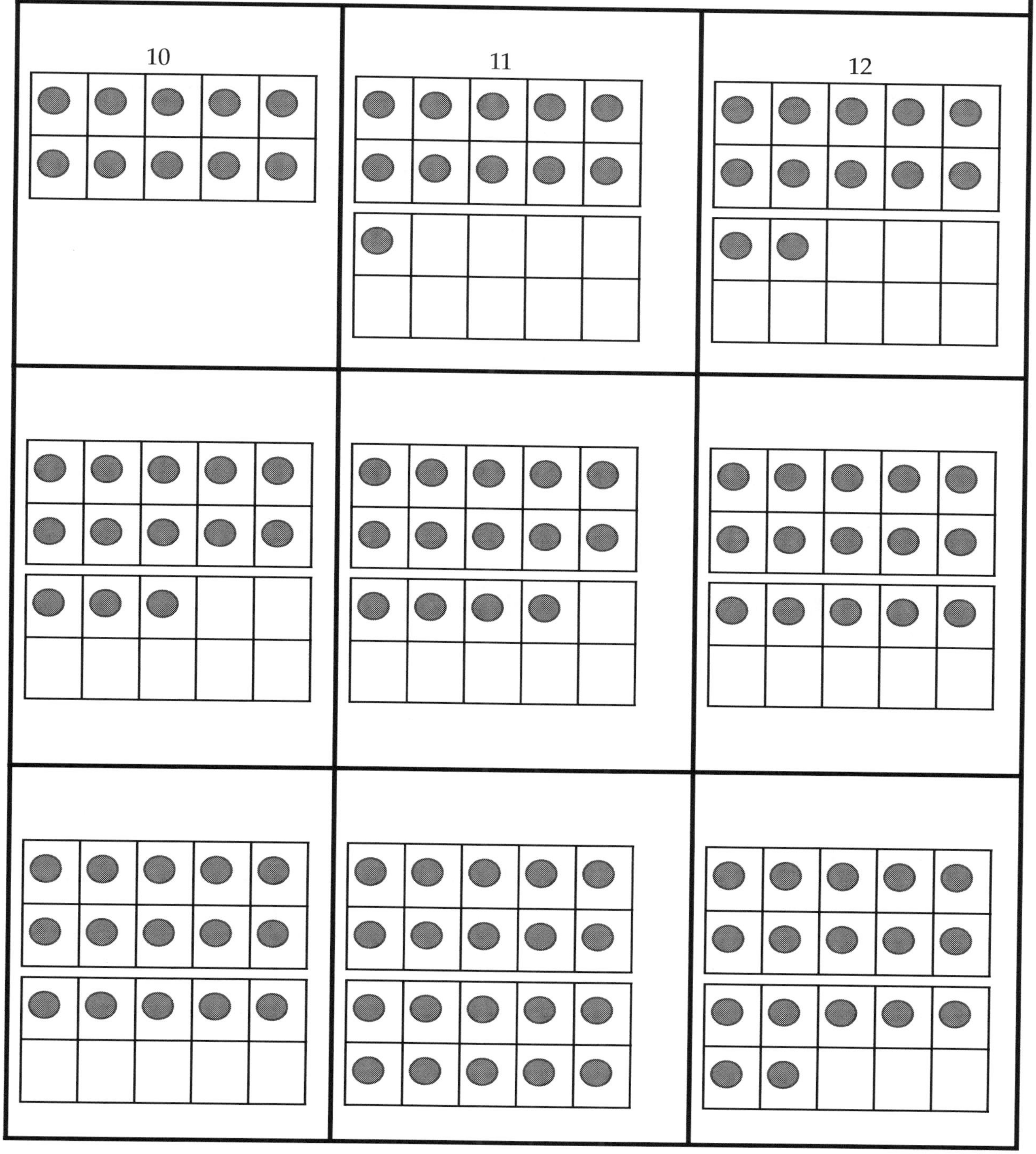

Figure 8.18 Ten Frame Recording Sheets

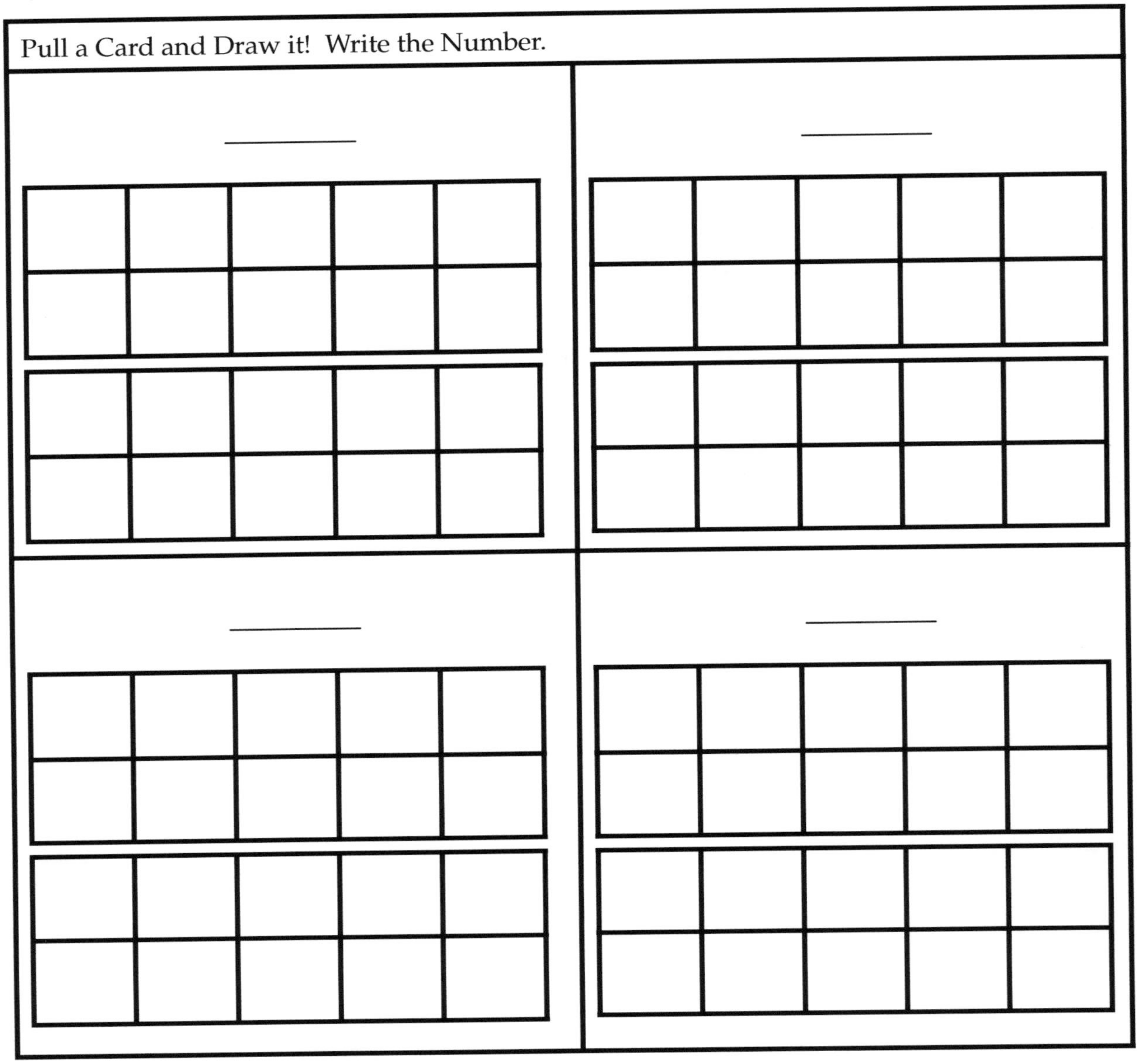

Pull a Card and Draw it! Write the Number.

_____

_____

_____

_____

Abstract Lesson

Figure 8.19 Abstract Introduction

Introduction to Abstract Explorations

Launch	**Teacher:** Today we are going to continue to work on teen numbers. **Vocabulary: model, teen number, tens, ones** **Math Talk:** _____ and ____ make _____. _____ + _____ = _____
Model	**Teacher:** Today we are going to continue to work on teen numbers. Today we are going to take turns trying to match the picture and the number. It is a match game. Whoever gets the most matches wins. Is this a match? **Hong:** No, because that's 10 and this is 11. **Kelli:** That is a match. 14 and 14!
Checking for Understanding	**Teacher:** Who can explain the game? **Mark:** I can. We pull 2 cards. They have to match **Teacher:** Ok, any questions? Ok, let's start.

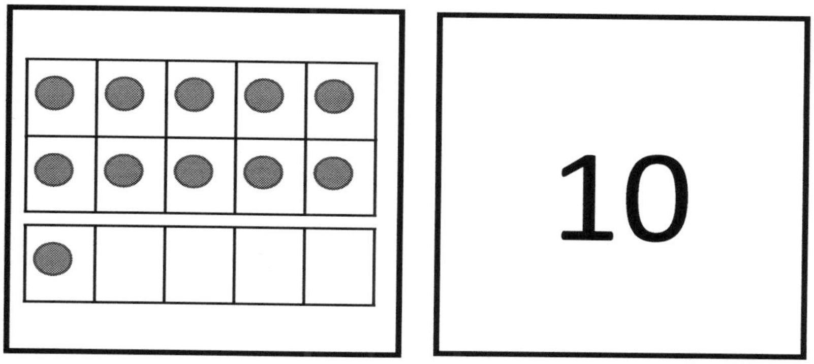

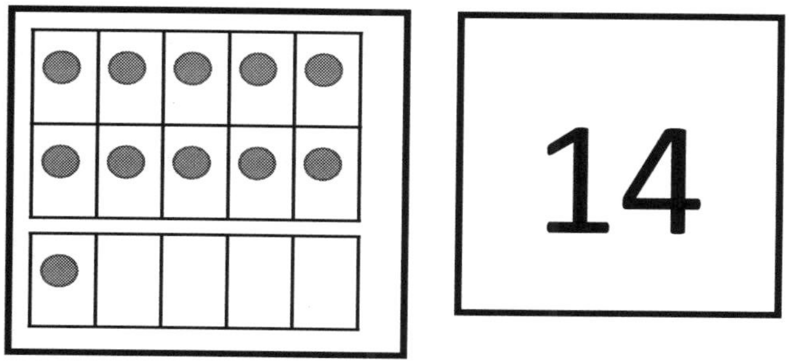

Figure 8.20 Student Activity

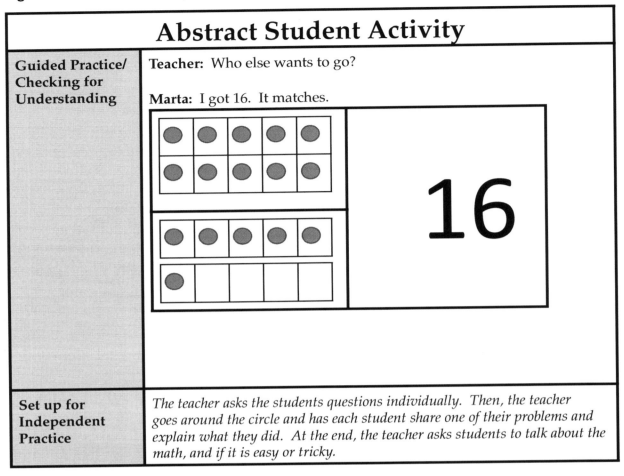

Abstract Student Activity	
Guided Practice/ Checking for Understanding	Teacher: Who else wants to go? Marta: I got 16. It matches. 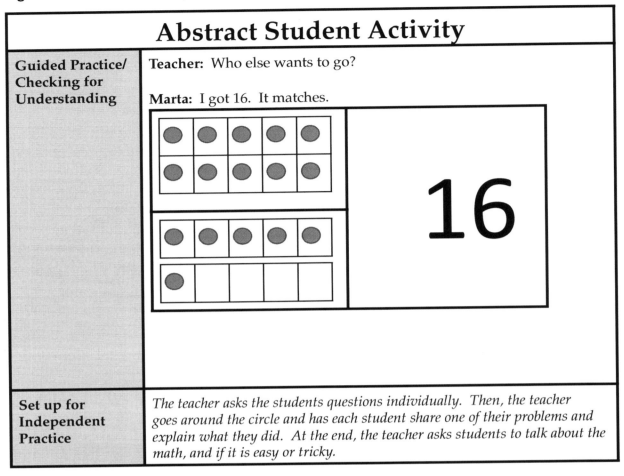
Set up for Independent Practice	*The teacher asks the students questions individually. Then, the teacher goes around the circle and has each student share one of their problems and explain what they did. At the end, the teacher asks students to talk about the math, and if it is easy or tricky.*

Figure 8.21 Lesson Close

Close
◆ What did we do today? ◆ What was the math we were practicing? ◆ Was this easy or tricky? ◆ Turn to a partner and state one thing you learned today.

Figure 8.22 Ten Frame Playing Cards

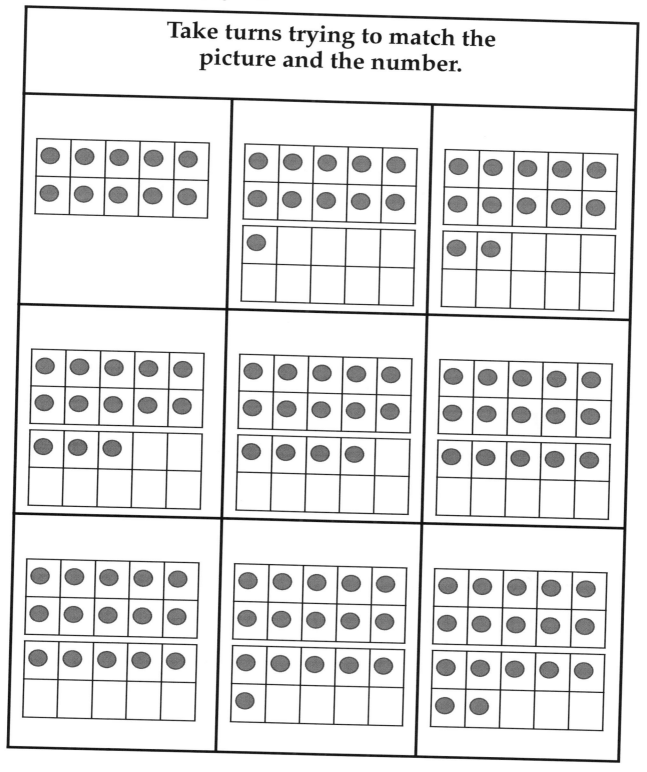

There are three possible levels to this game. The first level is where students are matching the number cards and the pictures. The second level is where the students are matching the place value statement and the pictures. The third level could be where they match all three cards.

Figure 8.23 Teen Playing Card

11	12	13	14	15
10	19	18	17	16

Figure 8.24 Verbal Statement Cards

10 and 1	10 and 2
10 and 3	10 and 4
10 and 5	10 and 6
10 and 7	10 and 8
10 and 9	10 and 0

Section Summary

It is very important for students to have an opportunity to see how ten singles can become 1 ten. Using ten frames is a great way to get students to explore this because they can see as they are building it how the ten ones become 1 ten. Throughout these lessons we will work with both the groupables and the pregrouped item. It is important for students to be able to build the model and then draw it. After this, they start to practice abstract games where they are matching the numeral with the visual exploration.

Teen Numbers on the Rekenrek

Overview

Figure 8.25 Overview

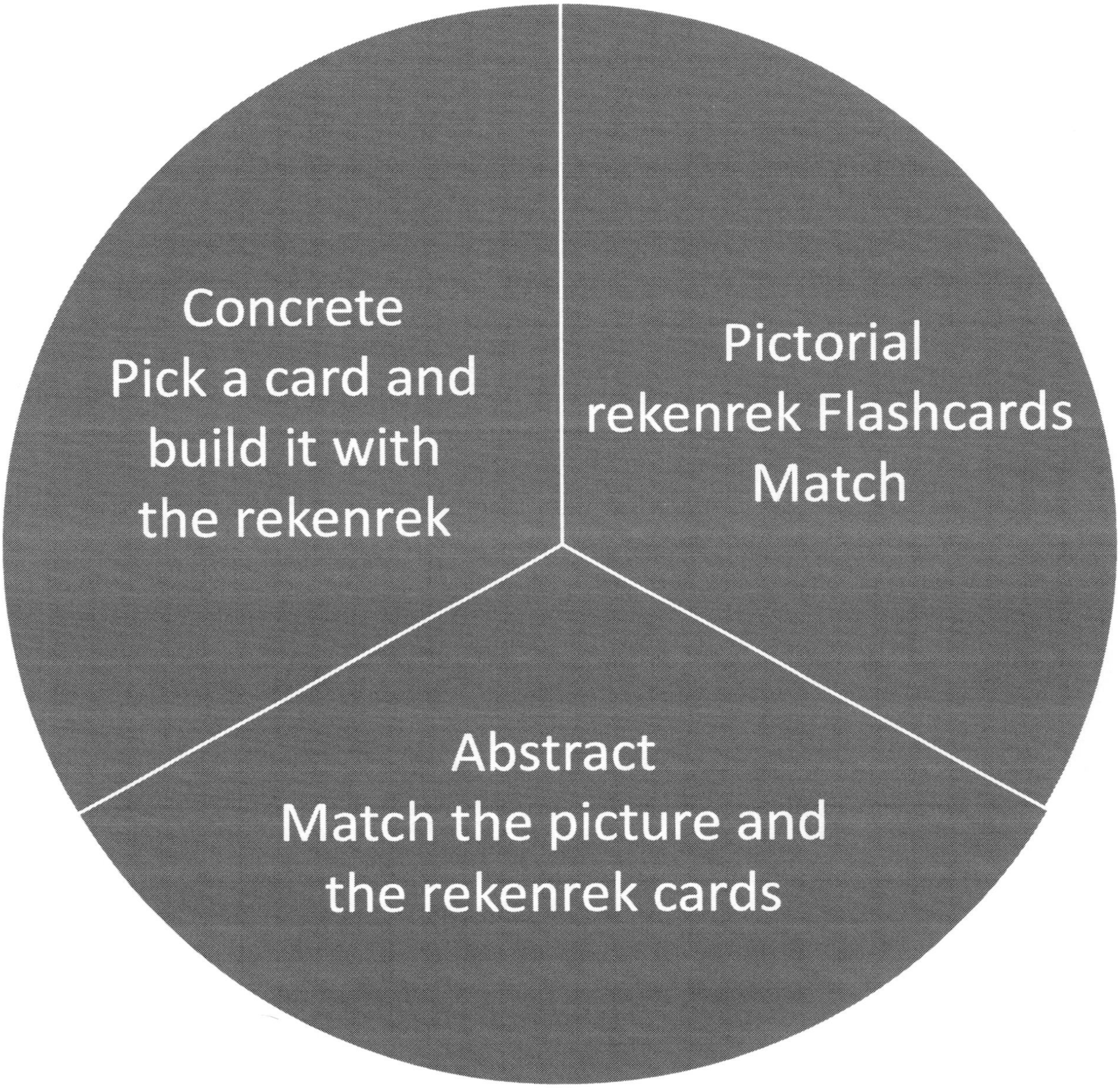

Concrete
Pick a card and build it with the rekenrek

Pictorial
rekenrek Flashcards Match

Abstract
Match the picture and the rekenrek cards

Figure 8.26 Planning Template

Exploring Place Value with Rekenreks

Big Idea: Tens and Ones

Enduring Understanding: A number can be 1 group of a ten and remainders

Essential Question: How can we represent teen numbers?

Content Question: What is a teen number? How can you break a teen number up into tens and ones?

I can statement:
I can recognize and name teen numbers.
I can build teen numbers.
I can draw teen numbers.

Materials
♦ Tools: Rekenrek
♦ Rekenrek Paper
♦ Templates: Ten Frame
♦ Cards
♦ Crayons

Questions
♦ What are the names of teen numbers?
♦ How can I break a teen number into tens and ones?
♦ What do the leftovers mean?

Cycle of Engagement
Concrete: Rekenrek

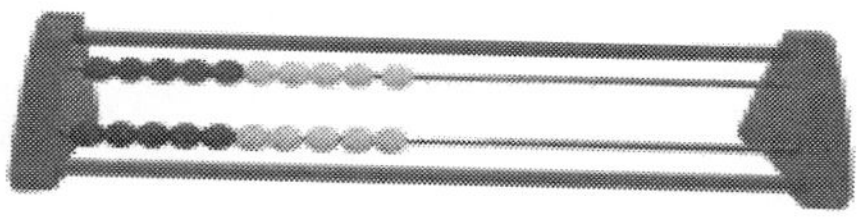

Pictorial:
Flashcards with numbers and pictures

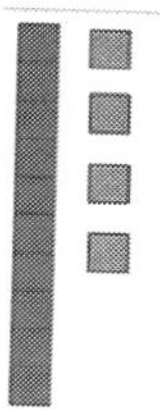

Abstract:
1 ten and 4 ones

Vocabulary & Language Frames

♦ Teen Number
♦ Model
♦ Ten
♦ Ones
♦ Leftovers

A 10 and _____ ones make the number _____

Figure 8.27 Differentiation

Three Differentiated Lessons
In this series of lessons, students are working on the concept of teen numbers using different types of models. They are developing this concept through concrete activities, pictorial activities and abstract activities. Here are some things to think about as you do these lessons.

Emergent Level	On Grade Level	Above Grade Level
Exploring grouping ones into a ten and remainders (11,12,13)	Use different models to represent expressions and equations of teen numbers.	Expand the number range.

 Looking for Misunderstandings and Common Errors

It is really important to work with groupable manipulatives where students can practice making tens and then counting the leftovers. They should have lots of opportunities to do this and then later on move to pregrouped items like the place value blocks.

Figure 8.28 Anchor Chart

We can model teen numbers in many ways!

Rekenreks:

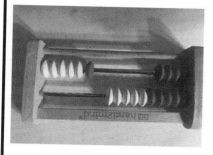

Rekenrek Paper

Draw What You Did on the Rekenrek!

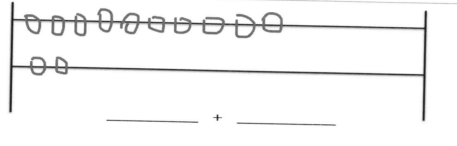

_____ + _____

Number Cards

12

Concrete Lesson

Figure 8.29 Concrete Introduction

<table>
<tr><td colspan="2" align="center">Introduction
Concrete Practice</td></tr>
<tr>
<td>Launch</td>
<td>

Teacher: Today we are going to work on exploring teen numbers with our rekenreks.

Vocabulary: model, teen number, tens, ones

Math Talk: _____ and ____ make _____. _____ + _____ = _____

</td>
</tr>
<tr>
<td>Model</td>
<td>

Teacher: Today we are going to work on representing/showing teen numbers with our rekenreks. How can we show a teen number with our rekenreks?

Jamal: It's like 13. You use a ten and 3 ones.

Teacher: Yes. Who can give me another example? 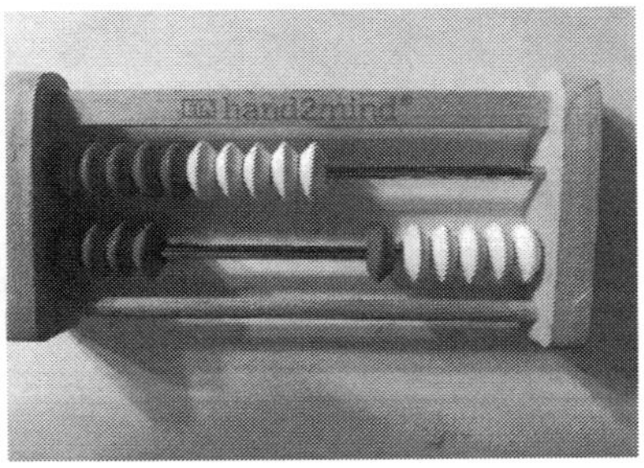

Tami: Like 12. 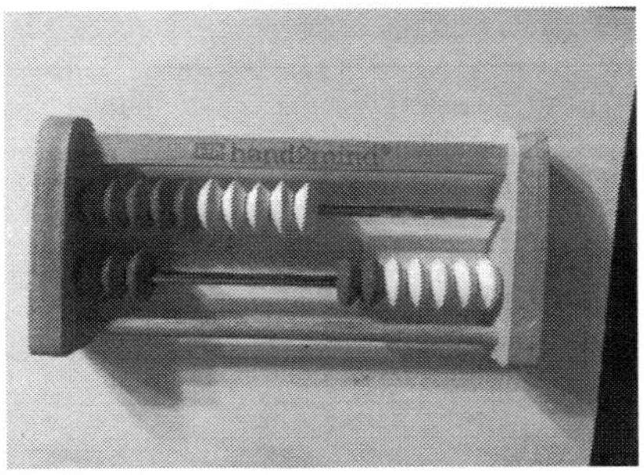

Teddy: You can show it with the a ten and then some leftovers.

</td>
</tr>
</table>

Checking for Understanding	**Teacher:** Excellent examples. They have a ten and some leftovers, like we have been talking about on the rug. Today we are going to build some on rekenreks. Here is the number: 14
	Kelli: I know…. It is 10 and then 4 left over.

	Teacher: Great!
	Teacher: Ok, smarty pants…. I am going to give you another one. 17 (the students build it). Ok, now I am going to give each one of you a number to build and then let you go around and say your number and explain how you built it.

Figure 8.30 Student Activity

	Concrete Student Activity
Guided Practice/ Checking for Understanding	The teacher passes out the rekenreks. You will build your number and then explain to the group your thinking. **Todd:** I had 16. I made 10 and then 6 leftovers.  **Teacher:** So what makes 16? **Melissa:** 10 and 6. **All the students get a chance to share their thinking.**
Set up for Independent Practice	*The teacher asks the students questions individually. Then, the teacher goes around the circle and has each student share one of their problems and explain what they did. At the end, the teacher asks students to talk about the math, and if it is easy or tricky.*

Figure 8.31 Lesson Close

Close
◆ What did we do today? ◆ What was the math we were practicing? ◆ Was this easy or tricky? ◆ Turn to a partner and state one thing you learned today.

Visual Lesson

Figure 8.32 Visual Introduction

<table>
<tr>
<td colspan="2" align="center"><h2>Introduction
Exploring with Visual Explorations</h2></td>
</tr>
<tr>
<td>Launch</td>
<td>Teacher: Today we are going to work on place value.

Vocabulary: model, tens, ones, teen number

Math Talk: _____ and _____ make _____. _____ + _____ = _____</td>
</tr>
<tr>
<td>Model</td>
<td>Teacher: Today we are going to pick a number and draw it on our rekenrek paper. See this is my card. I have 18.

Draw What You Did on the Rekenrek!

Harry: I want to go. I drew 11.

Draw What You Did on the Rekenrek!
</td>
</tr>
<tr>
<td>Checking for Understanding</td>
<td>Teacher: Who else wants to go?
Marta: I got 13. I have 1 ten and 3 leftovers.
Teacher: Ok, I am going to give you a baggie with cards and a recording mat. I want you to write the number and represent/show it. I am going to be asking you questions about your work.</td>
</tr>
</table>

Figure 8.33 Student Activity

	Visual Student Activity
Guided Practice/ Checking for Understanding	**Teacher:** Who else wants to go? **Marisol** I got 19. I have 1 ten and 9 leftovers. 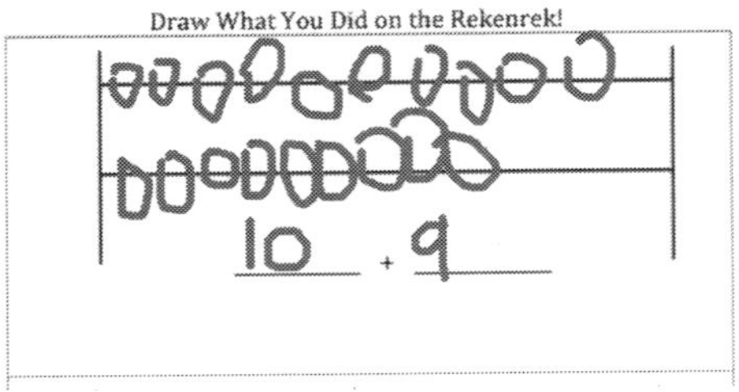 Draw What You Did on the Rekenrek! 10 + 9 **Teacher:** Tell me about your picture. **Marisol:** I pulled 19 so I drew 10 on the top and 9 on the bottom. It's almost 20. **Teacher:** What do you mean? **Marisol:** It's a ten and 9 ones. If I put 1 more it would be 20. **Teacher:** Oh, so 19 is close to 20. It is near 20. It is almost 20. It is just before 20. *Kids start to giggle....*
Set up for Independent Practice	*The teacher asks the students questions individually. Then, the teacher goes around the circle and has each student share one of their problems and explain what they did. At the end, the teacher asks students to talk about the math, and if it is easy or tricky.*

Figure 8.34 Lesson Close

Close
◆ What did we do today? ◆ What was the math we were practicing? ◆ Was this easy or tricky? ◆ Turn to a partner and state one thing you learned today.

Figure 8.35 Number Cards

11	12	13	14	15
10	19	18	17	16

Figure 8.36 Rekenrek Recording Paper

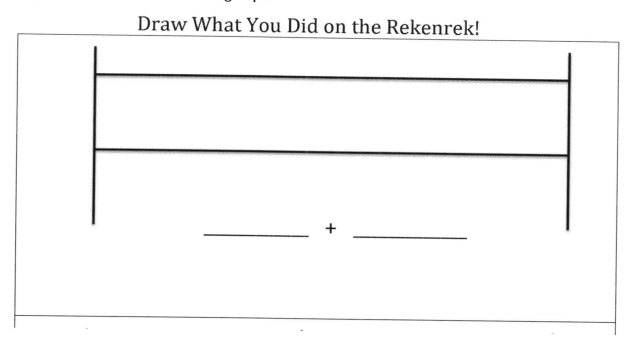

Draw What You Did on the Rekenrek!

_____ + _____

Abstract Lesson

Figure 8.37 Abstract Introduction

Introduction Abstract Exploration with Rekenreks and Number Cards

Launch	**Teacher:** Today we are going to continue to work on teen numbers.
	Vocabulary: model, teen number, tens, ones
	Math Talk: _____ and ____ make _____. _____ + _____ = _____
Model	**Teacher:** Today we are going to continue to work on teen numbers. Today we are going to play a compare game. It's called *Who has more? So both you and your partner will pick a card and build it on the rekenrek.* Whoever has more gets to keep both cards. At the end of the game, whoever has the most cards, wins.
	Kelli and Jackie.
	Jackie: I picked 14 and I have more. I have 4 leftovers!
	Kelli: I only have 1 left over.
	Jackie: I win both the cards.
	<table><tr><td>**14**</td><td>**11**</td></tr></table>
Checking for Understanding	**Teacher:** Who can explain the game? **Mark:** I can. We pull 2 cards. We build it. **Terri:** We compare. **Todd:** The big number wins both. **Kim:** They keep the cards. **Teacher:** Ok, any questions? Let's start.

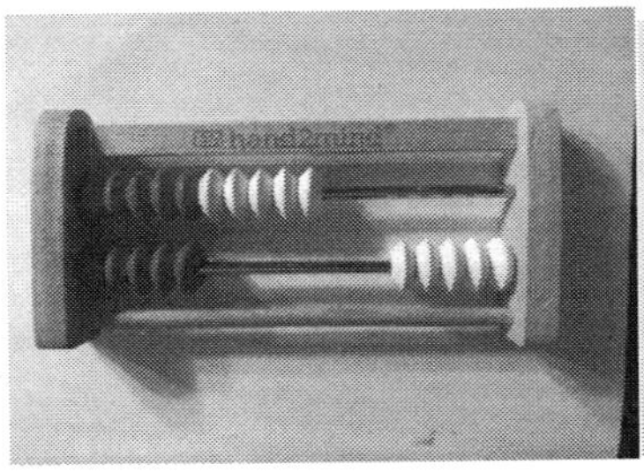

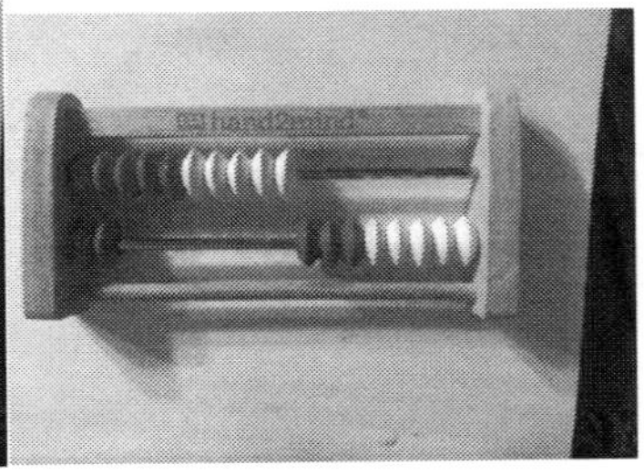

Figure 8.38 Student Activity

	Abstract Student Activity
Guided Practice/ Checking for Understanding	*The teacher watches as the partners play and asks them to explain their thinking.* **Teacher:** Marta and Carol, tell me about your cards. **Marta:** I pulled 15 **Carol:** I pulled 19. I win the cards because I have more leftovers. See (she shows it on her rekenrek). ┌─────┬─────┐ │ **19** │ **15** │ └─────┴─────┘
Set up for Independent Practice	*The teacher asks all the students questions. Then, the teacher goes around the circle and has each pair share one of their problems and explain what they did. At the end, the teacher asks students to talk about the math, and if it is easy or tricky.*

Figure 8.39 Lesson Close

Close
◆ What did we do today? ◆ What was the math we were practicing? ◆ Was this easy or tricky? ◆ Turn to a partner and state one thing you learned today.

Section Summary

In this section students are working with another groupable manipulative. I love rekenreks because they can see how the ones make a ten. I am showing the *Hand 2 Mind* ones because I like to use these in small guided math groups and they come in a convenient set of four. However, you can make your own (check out my Pinterest rekenrek board). You can also buy them from other places such as Didax. It is important that students have plenty of opportunities to build teen numbers on the rekenrek and then also to have opportunities to draw out models on the rekenrek paper, Finally, comparing teen numbers with models is also important so they can use the model to explain their thinking about which numbers are greater or fewer and why.

Place Value Blocks

Overview

Figure 8.40 Overview

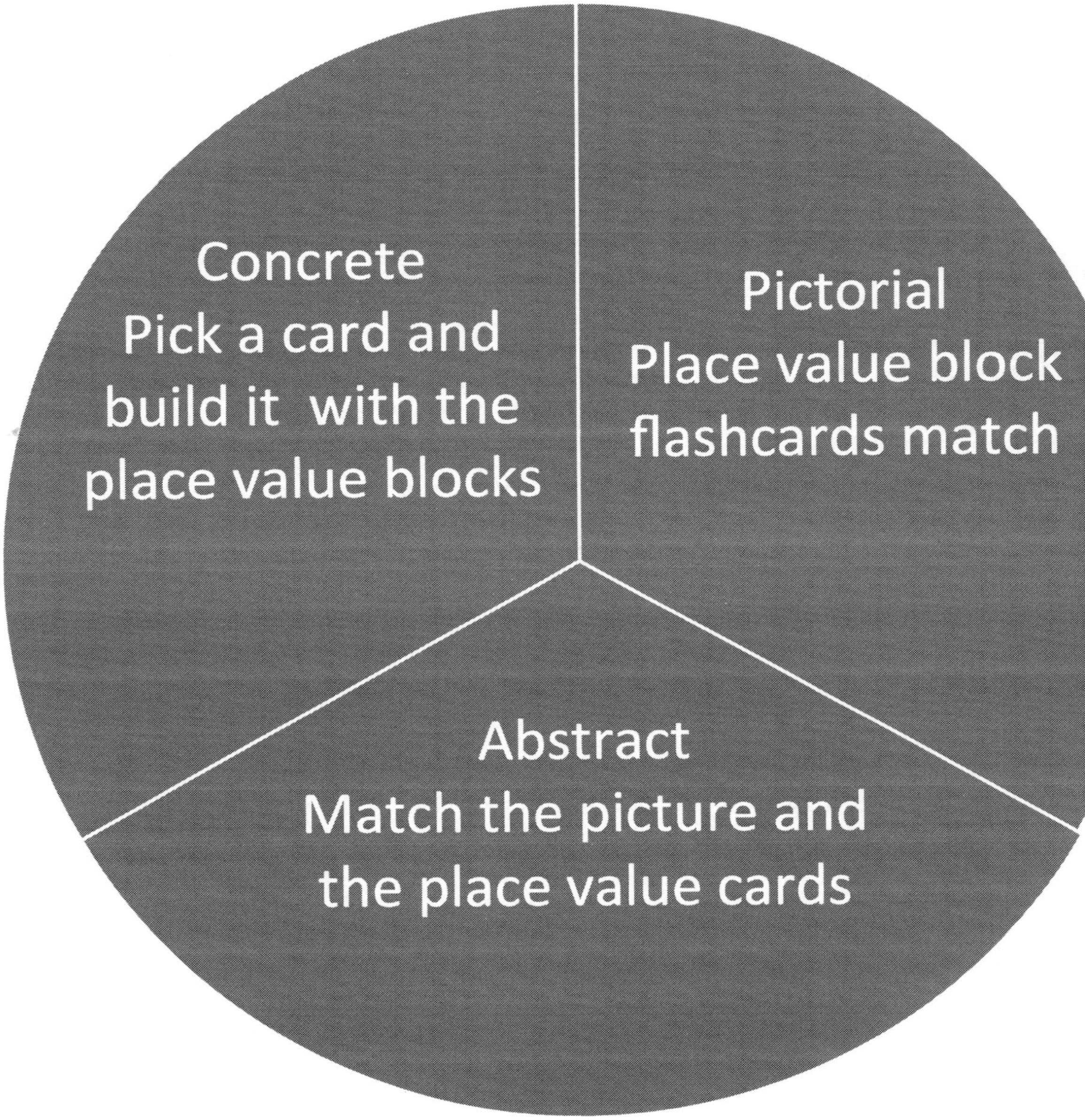

Concrete
Pick a card and
build it with the
place value blocks

Pictorial
Place value block
flashcards match

Abstract
Match the picture and
the place value cards

Figure 8.41 Planning Template

Exploring Place Value with Place Value Blocks

Big Idea: Tens and Ones

Enduring Understanding: A number can be 1 group of a ten and remainders

Essential Question: How can we represent teen numbers?

Content Question: What is a teen number? How can you break a teen number up into tens and ones?

I can statement:
I can recognize and name teen numbers.
I can build teen numbers.
I can draw teen numbers.

Materials
- Tools: Place value blocks
- Templates: Drawing place value blocks
- Cards
- Crayons

Questions
- What are the names of teen numbers?
- How can I break a teen number into tens and ones?
- What do the leftovers mean?

Cycle of Engagement

Concrete:

Pictorial:
Flashcards with numbers and pictures

14

Abstract:
1 ten and 4 ones

Vocabulary & Language Frames

- Teen Number
- Model
- Ten
- Ones
- Leftovers
- Remainders

10 and _____ones make the number _____

Figure 8.42 Differentiation

Three Differentiated Lessons
In this series of lessons, students are working on the concept of teen numbers using different types of models. They are developing this concept through concrete activities, pictorial activities and abstract activities. Here are some things to think about as you do these lessons.

Emergent Level	On Grade Level	Above Grade Level
Exploring grouping ones into a ten and remainders (11,12,13).	Use different models to represent expressions and equations of teen numbers.	Expand the number range.

 Looking for Misunderstandings and Common Errors

It is really important to work with groupable manipulatives where students can practice making tens and then counting the leftovers. They should have lots of opportunities to do this and then later on move to pregrouped items like the place value blocks.

Figure 8.43 Anchor Chart

We can model teen numbers in many ways!

Place Value Blocks

Sketches

Number Cards

14

Concrete Lesson

Figure 8.44 Concrete Introduction

<table>
<tr>
<td colspan="2"><h2 align="center">Introduction
Concrete Explorations</h2></td>
</tr>
<tr>
<td>Launch</td>
<td>Teacher: Today we are going to work on exploring teen numbers with our base ten blocks.

Vocabulary: model, teen number, tens, ones

Math Talk: _____ and ____ make _____. _____ + _____ = _____</td>
</tr>
<tr>
<td>Model</td>
<td>Teacher: Today we are going to work on representing/showing teen numbers with our base ten blocks. How can we show a teen number with our base ten blocks?
Jamal: It's like 16. You use a ten and 6 ones.

Teacher: Yes. Who can give me another example?

Tami: Like 11.

Teddy: You can show it with a ten on one side and then the leftovers.

Tens	Ones
▬	◻
▮	◻

</td>
</tr>
<tr>
<td>Checking for Understanding</td>
<td>Teacher: Excellent examples. They have a ten and some leftovers, like we have been talking about on the rug. Today we are going to build some on our place value mats. I am going to give you a mat and a baggie with some place value blocks so you can build a number that I show you. Here is the number: 12</td>
</tr>
</table>

Kelli: I know…. It is 10 and then 2 left over.

Tens	Ones
▬	▪
▮	▪ ▪

Teacher: Great!

Teacher: Ok, smarty pants…. I am going to give you another one. 17 (the students build it). Ok, now I am going to give each one of you a number to build and then let you go around and say your number and explain how you built it.

Figure 8.45 Student Activity

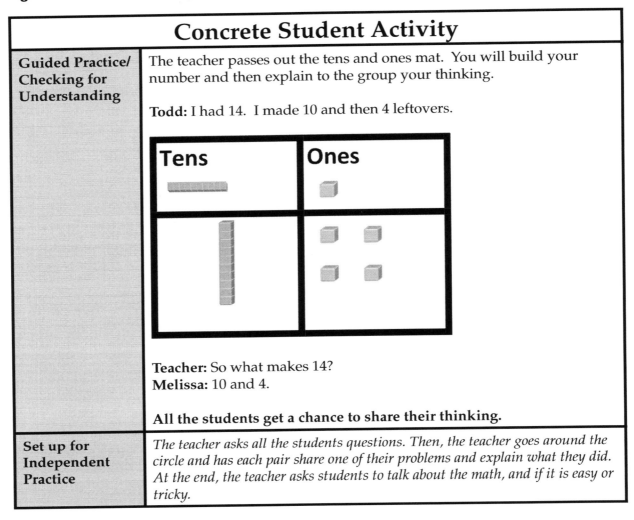

Concrete Student Activity	
Guided Practice/ Checking for Understanding	The teacher passes out the tens and ones mat. You will build your number and then explain to the group your thinking. **Todd:** I had 14. I made 10 and then 4 leftovers. **Tens** / **Ones** (diagram of base-ten blocks) **Teacher:** So what makes 14? **Melissa:** 10 and 4. **All the students get a chance to share their thinking.**
Set up for Independent Practice	*The teacher asks all the students questions. Then, the teacher goes around the circle and has each pair share one of their problems and explain what they did. At the end, the teacher asks students to talk about the math, and if it is easy or tricky.*

Figure 8.46 Lesson Close

Close
◆ What did we do today? ◆ What was the math we were practicing? ◆ Was this easy or tricky? ◆ Turn to a partner and state one thing you learned today.

Figure 8.47 Visual Introduction

	Introduction **Exploring with Visual Representations**
Launch	**Teacher:** Today we are going to work on place value. **Vocabulary:** model, tens, ones, teen number **Math Talk:** _____ and _____ make _____. _____ + _____ = _____
Model	**Teacher:** Today we are going to pick a number and draw it on our place value mat paper. See this is my card. I have 11. 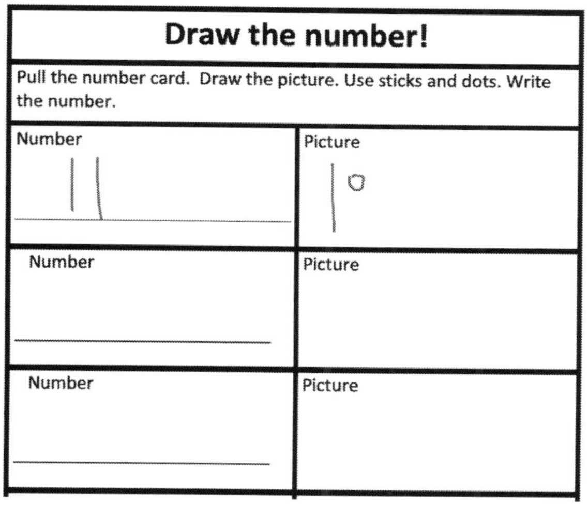 **Draw the number!** Pull the number card. Draw the picture. Use sticks and dots. Write the number. | Number	Picture
| |	| ○
Number	Picture
Number	Picture
	| **Harry:** I want to go. 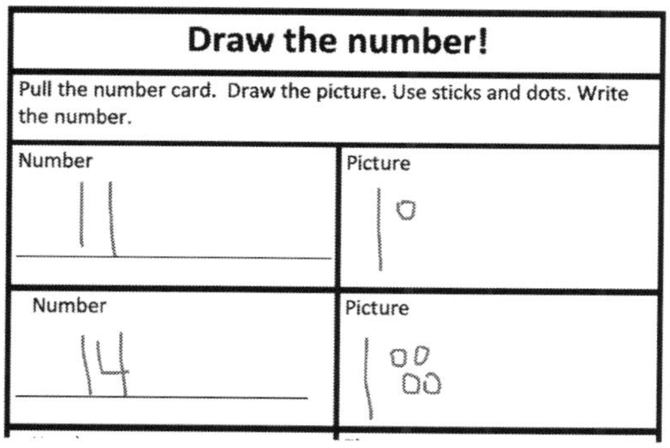 **Draw the number!** Pull the number card. Draw the picture. Use sticks and dots. Write the number. | Number	Picture
| |	| ○
Number	Picture
14	| ○○ ○○ | **Mike:** I will go. I got 14. I have 1 ten and 4 leftovers.

(Continued)

Figure 8.47 (Continued)

Checking for Understanding	Teacher: Who else wants to go?
	Marta: I got 13. I have 1 ten and 3 leftovers.
	Teacher: Ok, I am going to give you a baggie with cards and a recording mat. I want you to write the number and represent/show it. I am going to be asking you questions about your work.

Figure 8.48 Student Activity

	Visual Student Activity
Guided Practice/ Checking for Understanding	Teacher: Who else wants to go? Marisol I got 19. I have 1 ten and 9 leftovers. <table><tr><td colspan="2">**Draw the number!**</td></tr><tr><td colspan="2">Pull the number card. Draw the picture. Use sticks and dots. Write the number.</td></tr><tr><td>Number</td><td>Picture</td></tr><tr><td>Number</td><td>Picture</td></tr><tr><td>Number 9</td><td>Picture</td></tr></table> Teacher: Tell me about your picture. Marisol: I pulled 19 so I had to draw a stick and nine dots. Teacher: What does the stick and 9 dots mean? Marisol: It's a ten and 9 ones.
Set up for Independent Practice	*The teacher asks the students questions individually. Then, the teacher goes around the circle and has each student share one of their problems and explain what they did. At the end, the teacher asks students to talk about the math, and if it is easy or tricky.*

Figure 8.49 Lesson Close

Close
◆ What did we do today?
◆ What was the math we were practicing?
◆ Was this easy or tricky?
◆ Turn to a partner and state one thing you learned today.

Figure 8.50 Number Cards

11	12	13	14	15
10	19	18	17	16

Abstract Lesson

Figure 8.51 Place Value Block Recording Paper

Draw the number!	
Pull the number card. Draw the picture. Use sticks and dots. Write the number.	
Number _____	Picture
Number _____	Picture
Number _____	Picture
Number _____	Picture
Number _____	Picture

Figure 8.52 Abstract Introduction

	Introduction to Abstract Explorations with Place Value Blocks
Launch	**Teacher:** Today we are going to continue to work on teen numbers. **Vocabulary:** model, teen number, tens, ones **Math Talk:** _____ and ____ make _____. _____ + _____ = _____
Model	**Teacher:** Today we are going to continue to work on teen numbers. We are going to play a compare game. It's called **Who has more? So both you and your partner will pick a card and build it on the place value mat.** Whoever has more gets to keep both cards. At the end of the game, whoever has the most cards, wins. **Kelli and Jackie.** **Jackie:** I picked 14 and I have more. I have 4 leftovers! **Kelli:** I only have 1 left over. **Jackie:** I win both the cards. **11** **14**
Checking for Understanding	**Teacher:** Who can explain the game? **Mark:** I can. We pull 2 cards. We build it. **Terri:** We compare. **Todd:** The big number wins both. **Kim:** They keep the cards. **Teacher:** Ok, any questions? Ok, let's start.

Figure 8.53 Student Activity

	Abstract Student Activity
Guided Practice/ Checking for Understanding	*The teacher watches as the partners play and asks them to explain their thinking. Marta and Carol, tell me about your cards.* **Marta and Carol.** **Marta:** I pulled 15 **Carol:** I pulled 19. I win the cards because I have more leftovers. See (she shows it on her mat). <div align="center">**19** **15**</div>
Set up for Independent Practice	*The teacher asks all the students questions. Then, the teacher goes around the circle and has each pair share one of their problems and explain what they did. At the end, the teacher asks students to talk about the math, and if it is easy or tricky.*

Figure 8.54 Lesson Close

Close
◆ What did we do today?   ◆ What was the math we were practicing?   ◆ Was this easy or tricky?   ◆ Turn to a partner and state one thing you learned today.

Section Summary

In this section we have explored working with place value blocks which is a pregrouped manipulative. This would come later in the teaching trajectory, after students have had plenty of opportunities to practice unitizing—making groups of singles into a single ten. Students start by building numbers on their place value mats. Remember it is recommended that you color code the cards—for example, if the number 11 has the 10 in red and the 1 in blue and then the picture is color coded the same way it reinforces the place and value for the students. After they have plenty of time building it, they should then get to draw it with sticks and dots. Then the students practice comparing numbers with a scaffold of building them out on their mats if they need to.

Comparing Teen Numbers

Overview

Figure 8.55 Overview

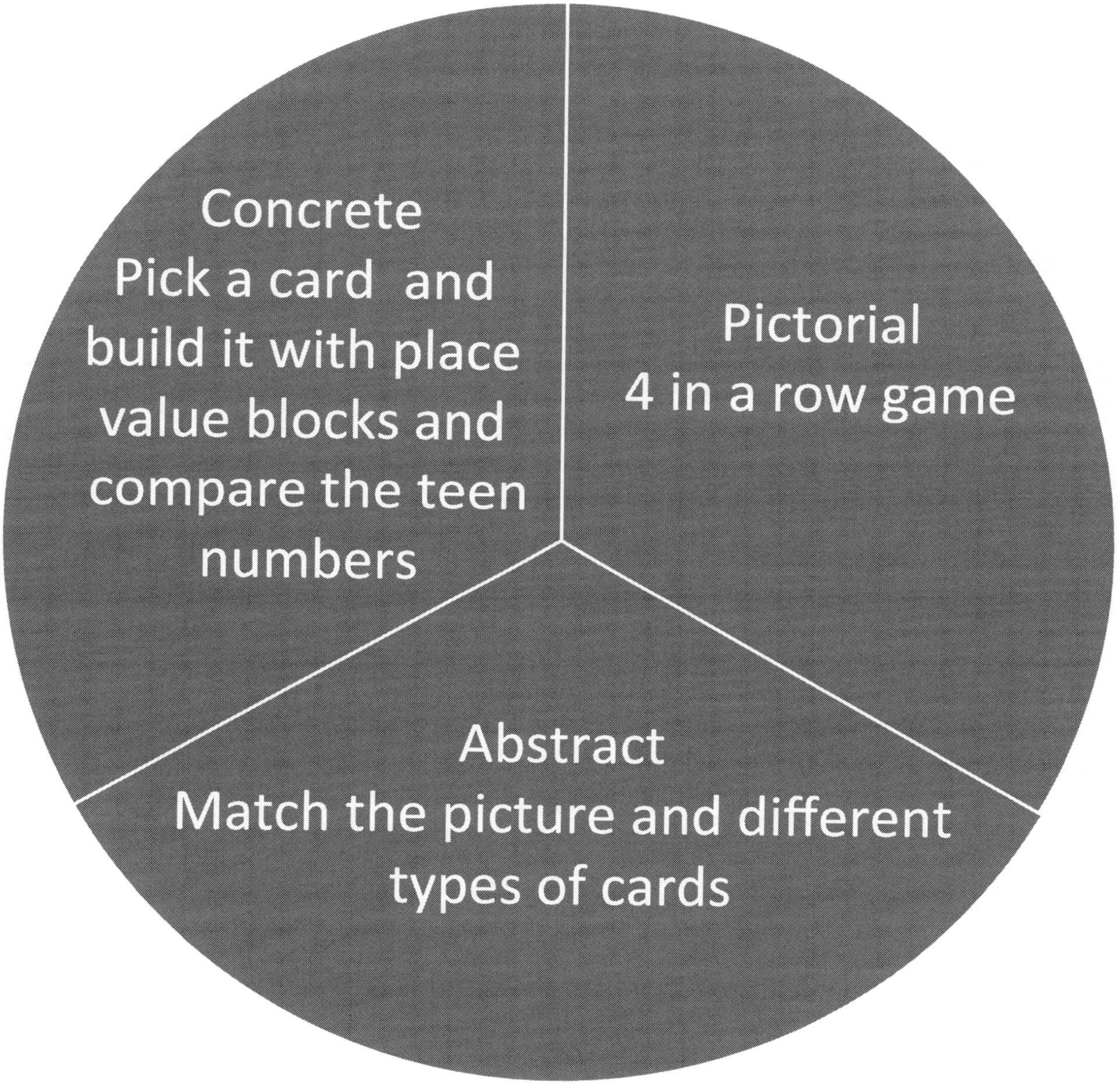

Concrete
Pick a card and build it with place value blocks and compare the teen numbers

Pictorial
4 in a row game

Abstract
Match the picture and different types of cards

Figure 8.56 Planning Template

Exploring Place Value with Place Value Blocks

Big Idea: Tens and Ones **Enduring Understanding:** A number can be 1 group of a ten and remainders **Essential Question:** How can we represent teen numbers? **Content Question:** What is a teen number? How can you break a teen number up into tens and ones? **I can statement:** I can recognize and name teen numbers. I can build teen numbers. I can draw teen numbers.	**Materials** ♦ Place value blocks ♦ Templates ♦ Cards ♦ Crayons <hr>**Questions** ♦ What are the names of teen numbers? ♦ How can I break a teen number into tens and ones? ♦ What do the leftovers/remainders mean?
<p align="center">Cycle of Engagement</p>**Concrete: Place Value Blocks**  **Pictorial:** **Flashcards with numbers and pictures**  **Abstract:** 1 ten and 9 ones	**Vocabulary & Language Frames** ♦ Teen Number ♦ Model ♦ Ten ♦ Ones ♦ Leftovers/ Remainders A 10 and _____ones make the number _____

Figure 8.57 Differentiation

Three Differentiated Lessons
In this series of lessons, students are working on the concept of teen numbers using different types of models. They are developing this concept through concrete activities, pictorial activities and abstract activities. Here are some things to think about as you do these lessons.

Emergent Level	On Grade Level	Above Grade Level
Exploring grouping ones into a ten and remainders (11,12,13).	Use different models to represent expressions and equations of teen numbers.	Expand the number range.

 Looking for Misunderstandings and Common Errors

It is really important to work with groupable manipulatives where students can practice making tens and then counting the leftovers/remainders. They should have lots of opportunities to do this and then later on move to pregrouped items like the place value blocks.

Figure 8.58 Anchor Chart

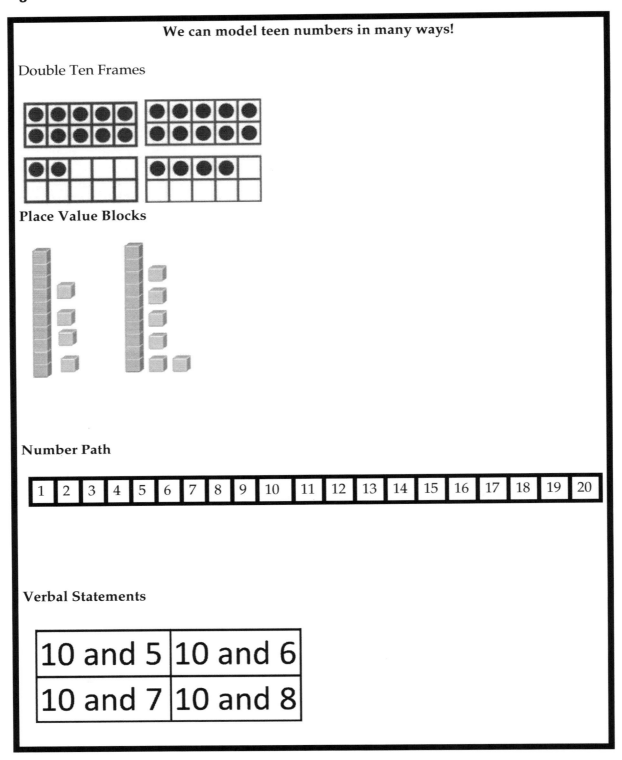

Concrete Lesson

Figure 8.59 Concrete Introduction

<table>
<tr>
<td colspan="2" align="center">Introduction
Concrete Practice</td>
</tr>
<tr>
<td>Launch</td>
<td>Teacher: Today we are going to work on comparing teen numbers with place value blocks.

Vocabulary: model, teen number, tens, ones, comparing, place value, leftovers

Math Talk: _____ is greater than _____.</td>
</tr>
<tr>
<td>Model</td>
<td>Teacher: Today we are going to work on comparing teen numbers. We will be pulling a number, building it and comparing it with a math partner.

Jackie: I pulled 15. 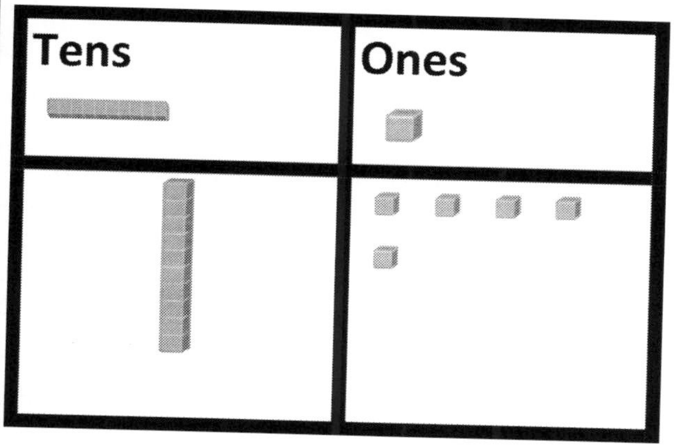

</td>
</tr>
</table>

Tim: I pulled 17. 17 is more than 15. I can prove it. See there are 7 leftovers here and only 5 on Jamal's mat.

Tens	Ones
▬	▫
▌	▫ ▫ ▫ ▫ ▫ ▫ ▫

Checking for Understanding	**Teacher:** Great!
	Teacher: Ok, smarty pants... You are going to play this game of build and compare with your partner. Whoever wins each turn gets to keep both number cards. Whoever has the most number cards at the end wins the game.

Figure 8.60 Student Activity

	Abstract Student Activity
Guided Practice/ Checking for Understanding	The teacher passes out the tens and ones mat. You will build your number and then explain to the group your thinking. **Todd:** I had 14. I made 10 and then 4 leftovers. <table><tr><td> 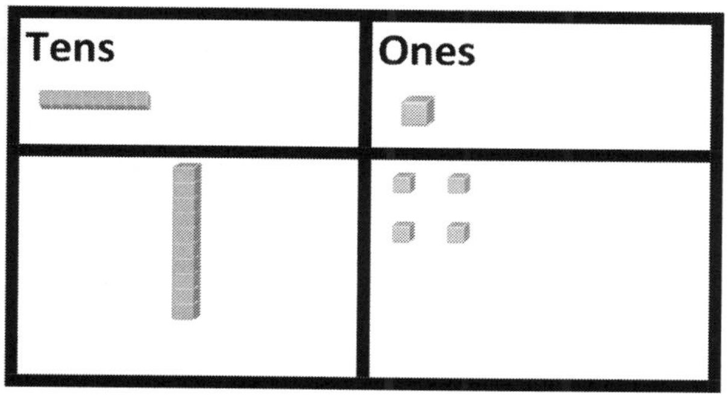**Tens**</td><td>**Ones**</td></tr><tr><td></td><td></td></tr></table> **Mary:** I pulled 11. So Todd has more left overs than me. 14 is greater than 11. <table><tr><td> 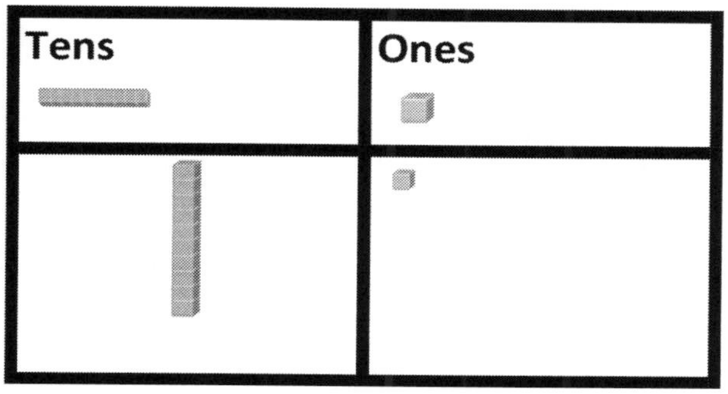**Tens**</td><td>**Ones**</td></tr><tr><td></td><td></td></tr></table>
Set up for Independent Practice	*The teacher asks the students questions individually. Then, the teacher goes around the circle and each student pair shares out one of their problems and explains what they did. At the end, the teacher asks students to talk about the math, and if it is easy or tricky.*

Figure 8.61 Lesson Close

Close
◆ What did we do today? ◆ What was the math we were practicing? ◆ Was this easy or tricky? ◆ Turn to a partner and state one thing you learned today.

Visual Lesson

Figure 8.62 Visual Introduction

	Introduction Exploring with Visual Representations
Launch	**Teacher:** Today we are going to work on place value. You and your partner are going to work together to cover the entire board. **Vocabulary: model, tens, ones, teen number** **Math Talk:** _____ and ____ make _____. _____ + _____ = _____
Model	**Teacher:** We are going to pick a number and cover it on our place value game mat. Who wants to go? **Hong:** I want to go. I got 19. I covered it. 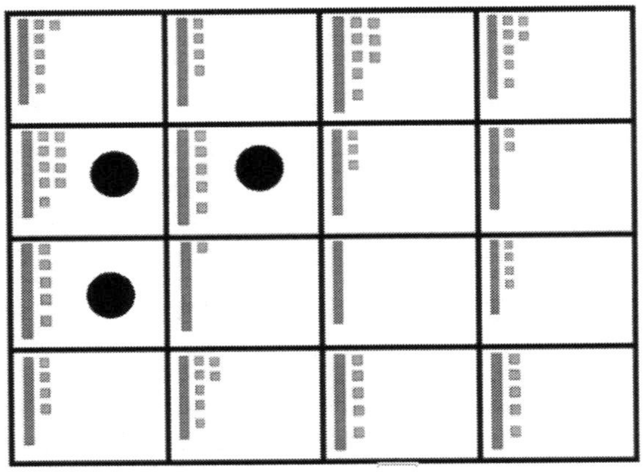 **Matt:** I will go. I got 15. I cover 15. **Maria:** I got 14 so I cover 14.
Checking for Understanding	**Teacher:** Ok, I am going to give you and your partner a baggie with cards, counters and a playing mat. I am going to be asking you questions about your work as you play the game.

Figure 8.63 Student Activity

	## Visual Student Activity
Guided Practice/ Checking for Understanding	**Teacher:** Marisol tell me how you know to cover 17. **Marisol:** I got 17. I have 1 ten and 17 leftovers. I mean 7 leftovers. 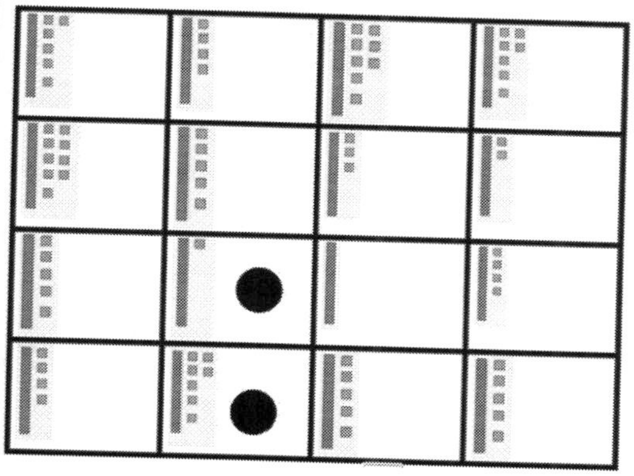 **Yesenia:** I got 11. I have 1 ten and 1 one.
Set up for Independent Practice	*The teacher asks the students questions individually. Then, the teacher goes around the circle and has each student pair shares one of their problems and explains what they did. At the end, the teacher asks students to talk about the math, and if it is easy or tricky.*

Figure 8.64 Lesson Close

Close
◆ What did we do today? ◆ What was the math we were practicing? ◆ Was this easy or tricky? ◆ Turn to a partner and state one thing you learned today.

Abstract Lesson

Figure 8.65 Abstract Introduction

	Introduction Abstract Exploration
Launch	**Teacher:** Today we are going to continue to work on teen numbers. **Vocabulary:** model, teen number, tens, ones **Math Talk:** _____ and ____ make _____. _____ + _____ = _____
Model	**Teacher:** Today we are going to continue to work on teen numbers. We are going to play a board game. You spin to see who has the lowest number. That person starts. Then, you spin to move around the board. You have to name the number where you land. Whoever reaches finish first wins.
Checking for Understanding	**Teacher:** Who can explain the game? **Maite:** I can. We move around the board land on a picture. Then, we have to name the number. **Teacher:** Ok, any questions? Ok, let's start.

Figure 8.66 Student Activity

	Abstract Student Activity
Guided Practice/ Checking for Understanding	The teacher watches the students as they play and asks them questions about their numbers. Students should say the name of the number and give a statement describing it. **Teacher:** Marta, tell me about where you landed. **Marta:** I landed on 11. It has 1 ten and 1 leftover. **Chase:** I landed on 12. It has 1 ten and 2 leftovers.
Set up for Independent Practice	*The teacher asks the students questions individually. Then, the teacher goes around the circle and has each student share one of their problems and explain what they did. At the end, the teacher asks students to talk about the math, and if it is easy or tricky.*

Figure 8.67 Lesson Close

Close
◆ What did we do today? ◆ What was the math we were practicing? ◆ Was this easy or tricky? ◆ Turn to a partner and state one thing you learned today.

Section Summary

In this section students begin to work on comparing teen numbers by building them and talking about the numbers. This is an activity that would come later on in the learning trajectory. The next activity is for the students to work together to pull a card and cover the representation. Remember that the cards should be color coded as previously discussed. The activity is a collaborative game because I really believe that students should play both collaborative and competitive games. The final game is a traditional board game where they travel around the board and have to state which number they land on and describe the number by saying . . . it has 1 ten and ___ leftovers.

Depth of Knowledge

Depth of Knowledge is a framework that encourages us to ask questions that require that students think, reason, explain, defend and justify their thinking (Webb, 2002). Here is a snapshot of what that can look like in terms of place value work. It is important to continually reflect on what the level of the lesson is. In working in small groups on problem solving, be sure to ask open questions so that students can think and reason out loud with others.

Figure 8.68 DOK Chart

	What are different strategies and models that we can use to model teen numbers?	More about teen numbers	How can we compare teen numbers?
Dok Level 1 (these are questions where students are required to simply recall/reproduce an answer/do a procedure)	What is a teen number?	Can you sequence these ten numbers from least to greatest? (Give the students all the teen numbers) Write the numbers between 11 and 20.	What is bigger, **11** or **14**?
Dok Level 2 (these are questions where students have to use information, think about concepts and reason) This is considered a more challenging problem than a level 1 problem.	Can you show 11 with ten frames?	$15 = 10 +$ 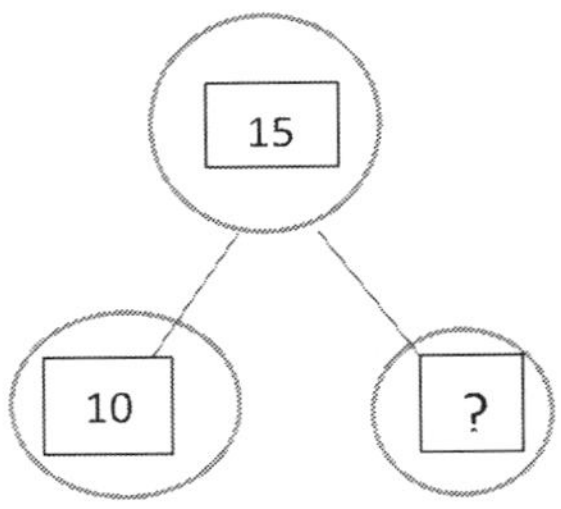 _____ 15 10 ?	What is a way that I could compare 2 teen numbers? What is a model that I could use to compare 2 teen numbers?
Dok Level 3 (these are questions where students have to reason, plan, explain, justify and defend their thinking)	Name and model a teen number. Explain how you know it is a teen number.	Describe what a leftover is? What does it tell us about a number?	Explain why 17 is smaller than 18. Show your thinking and defend your answer. Explain why 19 is greater than 12. Show your thinking and defend your answer.

Figure 8.69 Asking Rigorous Questions

DOK 1 Basic recall questions.	DOK 2 At this level students explain their thinking.	DOK 3 At this level students have to justify, defend and prove their thinking with objects, drawings and diagrams.
What is the answer to ??? Can you model the problem? Can you identify the answer that matches this equation?	How do you know that the equation is correct? Can you pick the correct answer and explain why it is correct? How can you model that problem in more than one way? What is another way to model that problem? Can you model that on the . . . ??? Give me an example of a . . . type of problem. Which answer is incorrect? Explain your thinking.	Can you prove that your answer is correct? Prove that . . . Explain why that is the answer. Show me how to solve that and explain what you are doing.

Resources

A great resource for asking open questions is Marion Small's *Good Questions: Great ways to differentiate mathematics instruction in the standards-based classroom* (2017). Also, Robert Kaplinsky has done a great job in pushing our thinking forward with the Depth of Knowledge Matrices he created (https://robertkaplinsky.com/depth-knowledge-matrix-elementary-math/). Kentucky Department of Education has a great DOK math matrix example also (2007).

Key Points

- ◆ Modeling with ten frames
- ◆ Modeling with rekenreks
- ◆ Modeling with place value blocks
- ◆ Comparing teen numbers

Chapter Summary

It is essential that we work on place value understanding with students in small guided math groups. We have to take them through the cycle of concrete, pictorial and abstract activities. We need to make sure that students understand, can explain and appropriately use the various models for representing teen numbers. Just because the textbook is teaching a specific model, in no way implies that the students are actually going to get it through just two or three days or even a week of working on that. Therefore, it is essential that we pull groups and work with students in their zone of proximal development. We then follow this work up with workstations and homework that correlates with the concepts they are working on. Place value should have the greater part of the spring devoted to reinforcing it.

Reflection Questions

1. How are you currently teaching place value?
2. Are you making sure that you do concrete, pictorial and abstract activities?
3. What do your students struggle with the most, and what ideas are you taking away from this chapter that might inform your work around those struggles?

References

Access Center. (2004). Concrete-representational-abstract Instructional Approach. *The Access Center* (pp. 1–6). Retrieved September 24, 2012 from www.k8accesscenter.org/training_resources/ documents/CRAApplicationFinal_000.pdf

Ainsworth, S. (1999). The Functions of Multiple Representations. *Computers & Education*, 33, 131–152.

Carpenter, T. P., & Lehrer, R. (1999). Teaching and Learning Mathematics with Understanding. In E. Fennema & T. Romberg (Eds.), *Mathematics Classrooms that Promote Understanding* (pp. 19–32). Mahwah, NJ: Lawrence Erlbaum Associates.

Fosnot, C. T., & Dolk, M. (2001). *Young Mathematicians at Work: Constructing Number Sense, Addition, and Subtraction.* Portsmouth, NH: Heinemann.

Ginsburg, H. P., Greenes, C., & Balfanz, R. (2003). *Big Math for Little Kids: Classroom Set.* Parsippany, NJ: Dale Seymour Publications.

Kentucky Department of Education. (2007). *Support Materials for Core Content for Assessment Version 4.1 Mathematics.* Retrieved January 15, 2017 from the internet.

McGuire, P., & Kinzie, M. (2013). Analysis of Place Value Instruction and Development in Pre-kindergarten Mathematics. *Early Childhood Education Journal*, 41(5). Retrieved December 5, 2020 from www.researchgate.net/publication/257557028_Analysis_of_Place_Value_Instruction_and_Development_in_Pre-Kindergarten_Mathematics

National Council of Teachers of Mathematics. (2000). *Principles and Standards for School Mathematics.* Reston, VA. Retrieved April 7, 2012 from http://standards.nctm.org/document/chapter4/numb.

National Research Council. (2009). Mathematics Learning in Early Childhood: Paths Toward Excellence and Equity. In C. T. Cross, T. A. Woods, & H. Schweingruber (Eds.), *Committee on Early Childhood Mathematics, Center for Education. Division of Behavioral and Social Sciences in Education.* Washington, DC: The National Academies Press.

Small, M. (2017). *Good Questions: Great Ways to Differentiate Math in the Standards Based Classroom.* New York: Teachers College Press.

Van de Walle, J. (2003). Developing Early Number Concepts and Number Sense. In *Elementary and Middle School Mathematics: Teaching Developmentally* (pp. 115–134). Boston, MA: Allyn & Bacon.

Webb, N. (2002). An Analysis of the Alignment between Mathematics Standards and Assessments for Three States. Paper presented at *the Annual Meeting of the American Educational Research Association*. New Orleans, LA.

9
Action Planning and FAQs

To get started, you must get started. So, pick where you want to start and just begin. Begin small. Here is an Action Checklist (see Figure 9.1).

Figure 9.1 Action Planning

Before the Lesson	
Decide on the topic that you want to do.	
Why are you doing this topic?	
Is this emerging, on grade level or advanced?	
Map out a three-cycle connected lesson plan.	
What are you going to do concretely?	
What are you going to do pictorially?	
What are you going to do abstractly?	
What misconceptions and error patterns do you anticipate?	
During the Lessons	
What are your questions?	
How are the students doing?	
What do you notice?	
What do you hear?	

DOI: 10.4324/9781003169529-9

What do you see?	
After the Lessons	
What went well?	
What will you tweak?	
What will you do the same?	
What will you do differently?	
What made you say "Wow!"	
What made you think "Uh-oh. . . . "	
What did you notice?	
What did you wonder?	
Other comments	

Frequently Asked Questions

1. **What is a guided math group?**
   Guided math is when you pull a temporary small group of students for instruction around a specific topic.

   Sometimes the groups are heterogeneous, and sometimes they are homogeneous. It depends what you are teaching. If you are teaching a specific skill, like adding within 10, and you have some students who know it and others who are struggling, then you would pull the students who need to learn it into a small group. However, sometimes you are working on general concepts, like modeling solving word problem with models. You can pull a heterogenous group to teach this.

2. **Why do guided math?**
   You do guided math for a variety of reasons. Lillian Katz said it best:

   > When a teacher tries to teach something to the entire class at the same time, chances are, one-third of the kids already know it; one-third will get it; and the remaining third won't. So two-thirds of the children are wasting their time.

   You do guided math so that everyone gets to learn. You can pull students for remedial work, on grade level work and enrichment. You do guided math so that students understand the math they are doing. You work with students in small groups so that they can talk, understand, reason and do math!

3. **What are the types of lessons?**
   There are five different types of guided math lessons.

   Conceptual, procedural, reasoning, strategy and disposition. Mostly disposition lessons are integrated throughout the other lessons, but sometimes you just pull students and talk about their journey. That could look like, *what is tricky about what we are learning?* And, *what is easy?*

4. **Do you always use manipulatives in a guided math group?**
   No. It depends where you are in the cycle of developing the concepts and student understanding. You certainly should use manipulatives in the beginning when you are developing concepts but eventually when students are practicing at the abstract level, they probably won't be working directly with manipulatives. Although, sometimes they still use them to check their answers or even solve problems if they need to.

5. **What about doing worksheets in guided math groups?**
   Never. It's simple. Guided math is students doing math, not doing a worksheet. Sometimes, you do pull students to work on some specific problems on a journal page but that is not the norm or the regular structure of a guided math group.

Reference

Katz, L. Retrieved April 15, 2019 from www.azquotes.com/author/39264-Lilian_Katz